The NSTA Reader's Guide to
A FRAMEWORK FOR K–12 SCIENCE EDUCATION

Practices, Crosscutting Concepts, and Core Ideas

Expanded Edition

National Science Teachers Association

Arlington, Virginia

National Science Teachers Association

Claire Reinburg, Director
Jennifer Horak, Managing Editor
Andrew Cooke, Senior Editor
Wendy Rubin, Associate Editor
Agnes Bannigan, Associate Editor
Amy America, Book Acquisitions Coordinator

SCIENCE AND CHILDREN
Linda Froschauer, Editor
Valynda Mayes, Managing Editor
Stefanie Muldrow, Associate Editor

THE SCIENCE TEACHER
Stephen Metz, Editor
Scott Stuckey, Managing Editor
Meg Streker, Associate Editor

ART AND DESIGN
Will Thomas Jr., Director
Cover photo provided by courtneyk for istockphoto.

SCIENCE SCOPE
Inez Liftig, Editor
Kenneth L. Roberts, Managing Editor

JOURNAL OF COLLEGE SCIENCE TEACHING
Ann Cutler, Editor
Caroline Barnes, Managing Editor

PRINTING AND PRODUCTION
Catherine Lorrain, Director
Jack Parker, Electronic Prepress Technician

NATIONAL SCIENCE TEACHERS ASSOCIATION
Francis Q. Eberle, PhD, Executive Director
David Beacom, Publisher

1840 Wilson Blvd., Arlington, VA 22201
www.nsta.org/store
For customer service inquiries, please call 800-277-5300.

Copyright © 2012 by the National Science Teachers Association.
All rights reserved. Printed in the United States of America.
15 14 13 12   6 5 4 3

NSTA is committed to publishing material that promotes the best in inquiry-based science education. However, conditions of actual use may vary, and the safety procedures and practices described in this book are intended to serve only as a guide. Additional precautionary measures may be required. NSTA and the authors do not warrant or represent that the procedures and practices in this book meet any safety code or standard of federal, state, or local regulations. NSTA and the authors disclaim any liability for personal injury or damage to property arising out of or relating to the use of this book, including any of the recommendations, instructions, or materials contained therein.

PERMISSIONS
Book purchasers may photocopy, print, or e-mail up to five copies of an NSTA book chapter for personal use only; this does not include display or promotional use. Elementary, middle, and high school teachers may reproduce forms, sample documents, and single NSTA book chapters needed for classroom or noncommercial, professional-development use only. E-book buyers may download files to multiple personal devices but are prohibited from posting the files to third-party servers or websites, or from passing files to non-buyers. For additional permission to photocopy or use material electronically from this NSTA Press book, please contact the Copyright Clearance Center (CCC) (*www.copyright.com*; 978-750-8400). Please access *www.nsta.org/permissions* for further information about NSTA's rights and permissions policies.

Library of Congress Cataloging-in-Publication Data

The NSTA reader's guide to A framework for K-12 science education. -- Expanded ed.
   p. cm.
   Includes bibliographical references.
   ISBN 978-1-936959-32-7 (print) -- ISBN 978-1-936959-75-4 (e-book) 1. Science--Study and teaching--Standards--United States. I. National Science Teachers Association. II. National Research Council (U.S.). Committee on a Conceptual Framework for New K-12 Science Education Standards. Framework for K-12 science education.
   LB1585.3.N77 2012
   507.1--dc23
                         2012010072

The NSTA Reader's Guide to *A Framework for K–12 Science Education*
by Harold Pratt

Understanding *A Framework for K–12 Science Education:* Top Science Educators Offer Insight

The NSTA Reader's Guide to A FRAMEWORK FOR K–12 SCIENCE EDUCATION

Practices, Crosscutting Concepts, and Core Ideas

Expanded Edition

By Harold Pratt

Background

In July 2011, the National Research Council (NRC) released *A Framework for K–12 Science Education: Practices, Crosscutting Concepts, and Core Ideas**, which identifies key scientific ideas and practices all students should learn by the end of high school. The *Framework* serves as the foundation for new K–12 science education standards that will replace those developed in the 1990s, including *National Science Education Standards* (*NSES*) and *Benchmarks for Science Literacy* (*Benchmarks*).

A state-led effort to develop the new science standards—called *Next Generation Science Standards (NGSS)*—is under way. Managed by Achieve Inc., the process involves science experts, science teachers, and other science education partners. The first draft of the *NGSS* will not appear until sometime in 2012, and the final version most likely will not appear until late in the year. In the meantime, NSTA recommends that the science education community fully examine the *Framework* and explore in-depth the concepts and ideas on which the new standards will be built.

Editor's Note: The tables and page numbers referenced in this document refer to the pre-publication copy of the *Framework* released in July 2011. A final print version will be released by the National Academies Press in late 2011 or early 2012 and will most likely have a different page numbering system. NSTA plans to update this *Guide*, including the page numbers, when the final *Framework* is printed. Check the NSTA website at *www.nsta.org/ngss* for updated information.

---

* National Research Council (NRC). 2011. *A Framework for K–12 Science Education: Practices, Crosscutting Concepts, and Core Ideas*. Washington, DC: National Academies Press.

Using This Guide

This guide is intended for many audiences—including science teachers, science supervisors, curriculum developers, administrators, and other stakeholders in science education—to help them better understand and effectively implement the new standards when they are released.

As the introduction to the *Framework* states, "the framework is intended as a guide to standards developers as well as to curriculum designers, assessment developers, state and district science administrators, professionals responsible for science-teacher education, and science educators working in informal settings" (p. 1-1). Teachers play a key leadership role in each of these functions and will benefit from a deep understanding of the *Framework* as a stand-alone document and as a guide to the use of the forthcoming *NGSS*.

To make the best use of this guide, the reader should have a copy of the *Framework* in hand for reference. The *Framework*, and many other NRC reports noted in this document, can be downloaded free of charge from the National Academies Press at *www.nap.edu*. This guide is designed to facilitate the study of the *Framework*, not replace reading it. For each chapter of the *Framework*, the guide provides

1. an overview;
2. an analysis of what is similar to and what is different from previous standards and benchmarks; and
3. a suggested action for science teachers, science supervisors, and other science educators to support understanding of the *Framework* and anticipate its impact on classrooms, schools, and districts.

Contents of the *Framework*

The overview is not intended to be an exhaustive summary of the *Framework* chapter, but rather a brief synopsis of the key idea(s). The second section—an analysis of what is new and different—is much more effective if the reader of this guide has a copy of the *NSES* and *Benchmarks* in hand or is reasonably familiar with these documents. Much of our analysis is based on comparisons with these two important documents that were published in the mid-1990s. Other documents also will be referenced to provide additional background and reading. The third section—suggested action—contains recommendations for activities for individuals, small teams, or larger groups to explore and learn about the ideas and concepts in the *Framework*. While some will find the overview and analysis sections most insightful, others will appreciate the suggested actions and use them as guides for possible professional development ideas.

The Three Dimensions
of the *Framework*

1. Scientific and Engineering Practices

- Asking questions (for science) and defining problems (for engineering)
- Developing and using models
- Planning and carrying out investigations
- Analyzing and interpreting data
- Using mathematics and computational thinking
- Constructing explanations (for science) and designing solutions (for engineering)
- Engaging in argument from evidence
- Obtaining, evaluating, and communicating information

2. Crosscutting Concepts

- Patterns
- Cause and effect: Mechanism and explanation
- Scale, proportion, and quantity
- Systems and system models
- Energy and matter: Flows, cycles, and conservation
- Structure and function
- Stability and change

3. Disciplinary Core Ideas

Physical Sciences
  PS 1: Matter and its interactions
  PS 2: Motion and stability: Forces and interactions
  PS 3: Energy
  PS 4: Waves and their applications in technologies for information transfer
Life Sciences
  LS 1: From molecules to organisms: Structures and processes
  LS 2: Ecosystems: Interactions, energy, and dynamics
  LS 3: Heredity: Inheritance and variation of traits
  LS 4: Biological evolution: Unity and diversity
Earth and Space Sciences
  ESS 1: Earth's place in the universe
  ESS 2: Earth's systems
  ESS 3: Earth and human activity
Engineering, Technology, and the Applications of Science
  ETS 1: Engineering design
  ETS 2: Links among engineering, technology, science, and society

Source: NRC 2011, p. ES-3

Executive Summary

The executive summary states the purpose and overarching goal of the *Framework*: to "ensure that by the end of 12th grade, *all* students have some appreciation of the beauty and wonder of science; possess sufficient knowledge of science and engineering to engage in public discussions on related issues; are careful consumers of scientific and technological information related to their everyday lives; are able to continue to learn about science outside school; and have the skills to enter careers of their choice, including (but not limited to) careers in science, engineering, and technology" (p. ES-1).

The *Framework* recommends that science education be built around three major dimensions, which are provided in the sidebar (Box ES.1, p. ES3)

The intent is that the *NGSS* should integrate these three dimensions. The early sections of the *Framework* do not communicate this intent, but it becomes clear in Chapter 9, "Integrating the Three Dimensions," and in the Chapter 12 recommendations to Achieve Inc. The early chapters are instead designed to provide an understanding of each separate dimension.

PART I:
A Vision for K–12 Science Education

Chapter 1
Introduction: A New Conceptual *Framework*

Overview

The best description of the general vision of the *Framework* is provided on page 1-2:

> The framework is designed to help realize a vision for education in the sciences and engineering in which students, over multiple years of school, actively engage in science and engineering practices and apply crosscutting concepts to deepen their understanding of the core ideas in these fields. The learning experiences provided for students should engage them with fundamental questions about the world and with how scientists have investigated and found answers to those questions. Throughout the K–12 grades, students should have the opportunity to carry out scientific investigations and engineering design projects related to the disciplinary core ideas.

> By the end of the 12th grade, students should have gained sufficient knowledge of the practices, crosscutting concepts, and core ideas of science and engineering to engage in public discussions on science-related issues, to be critical consumers of scientific information related to their everyday lives, and to continue to learn about science throughout their lives. They should come to appreciate that science and the current scientific understanding of the world are the result of many hundreds of years of creative human endeavor. It is especially important to note that the above goals are for all students, not just those who pursue careers in science, engineering, or technology or those who continue on to higher education.

Also from the introduction (p. 1-2),

> The committee's vision takes into account two major goals for K–12 science education: (1) educating all students in science and engineering and (2) providing the foundational knowledge for those who will become the scientists, engineers, technologists, and technicians of the future. The framework principally concerns itself with the first task—what all students should know in preparation for their individual lives and for their roles as citizens in this technology-rich and scientifically complex world.

The chapter discusses the rationale for including engineering and technology and for the exclusion of the social, behavioral, and economic sciences. It also includes a brief description of how the *Framework* was developed by the NRC committee.

Analysis

The stated vision reinforces what has been well accepted as the vision for science education for the past two decades and is clearly articulated in the *NSES* and *Benchmarks*.

A major difference you will notice is that the *Framework* introduces and defines engineering and technology and outlines the reasons for their inclusion in the *NGSS*.

What's also new is that to achieve the goal, the *Framework* moves science education toward a more coherent vision by (1) building on "the notion of learning as a developmental progression"; (2) focusing "on a limited number of core ideas in science and engineering"; and (3) emphasizing "that learning about science and engineering involves integration of the knowledge of scientific explanations (i.e., content knowledge) and the practices needed to engage in scientific inquiry and engineering design" (p. 1-3).

Suggested Action

Compare the *Framework*'s vision and overarching goals for science education to those of your state, school, or district. What differences do you find? A review and possible update by your curriculum committees might be in order because the nature of the vision and goals stated in the *Framework* will undoubtedly appear in the *NGSS*. Note the increased emphasis on how students learn science in the means or goals of how the vision will be achieved. This will be discussed in more detail in the next chapter.

Chapter 2
Guiding Assumptions and Organization of the *Framework*

Overview

The *Framework* defines several guiding principles about the nature of learning science that underlie the structure and content of the *Framework*. Below is a summary of these principles, adapted from pages 2-1 through 2-4.

Children are born investigators: In the early years of life, children engage in and develop their own ideas about the physical, biological, and social worlds and how they work and, thus, can engage in scientific and engineering practices beginning in the early grades.

Focusing on core ideas and practices: The *Framework* is focused on a limited set of core ideas to allow for deep exploration of important concepts and time for students to develop meaningful understanding of these concepts through practice and reflection. The core ideas are an organizing structure to support acquiring new knowledge over time and to help students build capacity to develop a more flexible and coherent understanding of science.

Understanding develops over time: Student understanding of scientific ideas matures over time—across years rather than in weeks or months—and instructional supports and experiences are needed to sustain students' progress.

Science and engineering require both knowledge and practice: Science is not just a body of knowledge that reflects current understanding of the world; it is also a set of practices used to establish, extend, and refine that knowledge. Both elements—knowledge and practice—are essential.

Connecting to students' interests and experiences: For students to develop a sustained attraction to science and for them to appreciate the many ways in which it is pertinent to their daily lives, classroom learning experiences in science need to connect with students' own interests and experiences.

Promoting equity: All students should be provided with equitable opportunities to learn science and become engaged in science and engineering practices—with access to quality space, equipment, and teachers to support and motivate that learning and engagement, and with adequate time spent on science.

The balance of the chapter outlines the structure of the *Framework* and its three dimensions—scientific and engineering practices, crosscutting concepts, and disciplinary core ideas—and their progressions across grades K–12.

Analysis

The introduction to this chapter lists the NRC publications *Taking Science to School* (Duschl, Schweingruber, and Shouse 2007), *America's Lab Report* (Singer, Hilton, and Schweingruber 2006), *Learning Science in Informal Environments* (Bell et al. 2009), *Systems for State Science Assessments* (Wilson and Bertenthal 2006), and *Engineering in K–12 Education* (Katehi, Pearson, and Feders 2009) that served as background for the writers of the *Framework*. These reports are based on research from the 15 years following the publication of the *NSES* and *Benchmarks* and represents an evolving knowledge of how students learn science and the nature of curriculum and instruction that will facilitate the learning. That increased level of knowledge about how students learn is reflected in the guiding principles outlined on the previous page.

Suggested Action

Obtain copies of the publications cited in this chapter and form study or discussion groups to become familiar with the research synthesized in them and their view of how students learn science. Explore how the research and ideas have changed since the publication of the *NSES* and *Benchmarks* and how they are reflected in the *Framework*. One of the best places to begin is with *How People Learn: Brain, Mind, Experience, and School* (Bransford, Brown, and Cocking 2000). This seminal work is easy to read, contains research on the broad topic of how learning occurs, and has a chapter with examples on how students learn science, mathematics, and history. In addition, a recent report that has had significant influence on the *Framework* is *Taking Science to School* (Duschl, Schweingruber, and Shouse 2007). This report provides the background for the Framework's guiding principles and helps explain the evolution from the language of inquiry to practices.

PART II:
Dimensions of the *Framework*

Chapter 3
Dimension 1: Scientific and Engineering Practices

Overview

This chapter continues and strengthens one of the principal goals of science education, "to engage in scientific inquiry" and "reason in a scientific context" (p. 3-1). In doing so, it explains the transition or evolution from inquiry to practices and discusses the reasons why practices are considered to be an improvement over the previous approaches.

The change is described as an improvement in three ways:

- "It minimizes the tendency to reduce scientific practice to a single set of procedures" (p. 3-2).
- By emphasizing the plural practices, it avoids the mistaken idea that there is one scientific method.
- It provides a clearer definition of the elements of inquiry than previously offered.

Scientific and Engineering Practices

Asking Questions and Defining Problems

A basic practice of the **scientist** is the ability to formulate empirically answerable questions about phenomena to establish what is already known, and to determine what questions have yet to be satisfactorily answered.	**Engineering** begins with a problem that needs to be solved, such as "How can we reduce the nation's dependence on fossil fuels?" or "What can be done to reduce a particular disease?" or "How can we improve the fuel efficiency of automobiles?"

Developing and Using Models

Science often involves the construction and use of models and simulations to help develop explanations about natural phenomena.	**Engineering** makes use of models and simulations to analyze systems to identify flaws that might occur or to test possible solutions to a new problem.

Planning and Carrying Out Investigations

A major practice of **scientists** is planning and carrying out systematic scientific investigations that require identifying variables and clarifying what counts as data.	**Engineering** investigations are conducted to gain data essential for specifying criteria or parameters and to test proposed designs.

Analyzing and Interpreting Data

Scientific investigations produce data that must be analyzed to derive meaning. Scientists use a range of tools to identify significant features and patterns in the data.	**Engineering** investigations include analysis of data collected in the tests of designs. This allows comparison of different solutions and determines how well each meets specific design criteria.

Using Mathematics, Information and Computer Technology, and Computational Thinking	
In **science,** mathematics and computation are fundamental tools for representing physical variables and their relationships.	In **engineering,** mathematical and computational representations of established relationships and principles are an integral part of the design process.

Constructing Explanations and Designing Solutions	
The goal of **science** is the construction of theories that provide explanatory accounts of the material world.	The goal of **engineering** design is a systematic approach to solving engineering problems that is based on scientific knowledge and models of the material world.

Engaging in Argument From Evidence	
In **science,** reasoning and argument are essential for clarifying strengths and weaknesses of a line of evidence and for identifying the best explanation for a natural phenomenon.	In **engineering,** reasoning and argument are essential for finding the best solution to a problem. Engineers collaborate with their peers throughout the design process.

Obtaining, Evaluating, and Communicating Information	
Science cannot advance if scientists are unable to communicate their findings clearly and persuasively or learn about the findings of others.	**Engineering** cannot produce new or improved technologies if the advantages of their designs are not communicated clearly and persuasively.

The *Framework* identifies eight practices that are essential elements of a K–12 science and engineering curriculum and describes the competencies for each practice. They are identified and described in "Scientific and Engineering Practices" above.

For each practice, the *Framework* includes a comparison of how the practice is seen in science and engineering, a list of student goals to achieve by grade 12, and a discussion of the progression to reach those goals from the early grades through grade 12. Box 3-2 (p. 3-29), "Distinguishing Practices in Science From Those in Engineering," provides a very useful three-page table.

The *Framework* repeatedly emphasizes that practices are not taught in isolation but are an essential part of content instruction. Consider this quote from page ES-1 (emphasis added): "the committee concludes that K–12 science and engineering education should focus on a limited number of disciplinary core ideas and crosscutting concepts, be designed so that students continually build on and revise their knowledge and abilities over multiple years, and support the *integration of such knowledge and abilities with the practices* needed to engage in scientific inquiry and engineering design."

Analysis

The notion of moving from the language of inquiry to that of practices, and the inclusion of engineering practices, will most likely require an adjustment or paradigm shift for many science educators. For the experienced teacher or science educator who is familiar with the inquiry standards in *NSES* and has helped students meet them through the use of "inquiries," the practices will not seem that foreign. The added details and explanations of the practices will be an advantage to many users.

The parallel discussion of each practice in both science and engineering does not imply that the two should be taught or learned at the same time, but rather intends to point out the similarities and differences among the practices in both disciplines. In some sense, the science practices have emerged from *Taking Science to School* (Duschl, Schweingruber, and Shouse 2007) and *Ready, Set, Science!* (Michaels, Shouse, and Schweingruber 2008), both of which provide a review of the research on how students learn science and how that can be used in the creation of teaching materials and classroom instruction. The *Framework* builds on this research and has identified engineering practices as a parallel discussion.

In past years, science practices have not received the same emphasis that has been placed on content knowledge, nor has the integration of content and inquiry been achieved to any great extent. The *NGSS* most certainly will include an equal and integrated emphasis. Consider this quote from page 2-3: "Science is not just a body of knowledge that reflects current understanding of the world; it is also a set of practices used to establish, extend, and refine that knowledge. Both elements—knowledge and practice—are essential." The integration of practices with the content will improve students' understanding of the concepts and purposes of science and will avoid the teaching and learning of the competencies of inquiry in isolation.

Suggested Action

The shift for most science educators in this area will be the movement from the language and standards of inquiry in the *NSES* to the language of practices and becoming familiar with the engineering practices. To gain a better understanding of engineering, obtain *Engineering in K–12 Education: Understanding the Status and Improving the Prospects* (Katehi, Pearson, and Feders 2009) and *Standards for K–12 Engineering Education?* (NRC 2010b), two of the many documents referenced at the end of this *Framework* chapter, and use them as resources for study and discussion. Both can be downloaded for free from the National Academies Press at *www.nap.edu*.

Compare the practices of inquiry in your instruction, instructional materials, and assessment to those in the *Framework* to see what may need to be added or spelled out in more detail. Notice the progression of the goals for each practice. Check your grade level for the practices against those in the *Framework*. To what extent are they integrated with the content in your curriculum? Since the *NGSS* will integrate the three dimensions (see Chapter 9), beginning to review how practices of inquiry are integrated in your existing instruction—as well as how they are aligned and progress from level to level—will enhance your ability to use the anticipated new standards.

Chapter 4
Dimension 2: Crosscutting Concepts

Overview

This chapter outlines the second dimension of the *Framework*, seven crosscutting concepts that have great value across the sciences and in engineering and that are considered fundamental to understanding these disciplines:

1. Patterns
2. Cause and Effect: Mechanism and Explanation
3. Scale, Proportion, and Quantity
4. Systems and System Models
5. Energy and Matter: Flows, Cycles, and Conservation
6. Structure and Function
7. Stability and Change

Analysis

Readers familiar with the *NSES* and *Benchmarks* will recognize that the *Framework*'s crosscutting concepts are similar to those in the Unifying Concepts and Processes in *NSES* and the Common Themes in *Benchmarks*. Although the previous documents call for the integration of these concepts with the content standards, the *Framework* specifically recommends, "Standards should emphasize all three dimensions articulated in the framework." (See Recommendation 4 in Chapter 12, p. 12-3.) This requirement will not only be a challenge to the writers of the *NGSS* but will also call for a major change in instructional materials and assessments.

Suggested Action

Participate in a review to determine if and how the Unifying Concepts and Processes in *NSES* and/or the Common Themes in *Benchmarks* are currently incorporated in your standards, curriculum, and instructional materials.

The list of crosscutting concepts in the *NGSS* will undoubtedly use the list in the *Framework*, making it possible to begin planning professional development to assist teachers in understanding and incorporating the concepts into their current teaching without waiting for the completion of the *NGSS*. The above review could serve as the impetus and needs assessment for the initiation and planning of the professional development. Exemplary instructional materials can serve as models and resources for the professional materials, but any adoption should await the release of the *NGSS*.

Chapter 5
Dimension 3: Disciplinary Core Ideas: Physical Sciences

Overview
The physical sciences section has been organized under the following four core ideas and 13 component ideas.

Core Idea PS1: Matter and Its Interactions
- PS1.A: Structure and Properties of Matter
- PS1.B: Chemical Reactions
- PS1.C: Nuclear Processes

Core Idea PS2: Motion and Stability: Forces and Interactions
- PS2.A: Forces and Motion
- PS2.B: Types of Interactions
- PS2.C: Stability and Instability in Physical Systems

Core Idea PS3: Energy
- PS3.A: Definitions of Energy
- PS3.B: Conservation of Energy and Energy Transfer
- PS3.C: Relationship Between Energy and Forces
- PS3.D: Energy in Chemical Processes and Everyday Life

Core Idea PS4: Waves and Their Applications in Technologies for Information Transfer
- PS4.A: Wave Properties
- PS4.B: Electromagnetic Radiation
- PS4.C: Information Technologies and Instrumentation

The *Framework* introduces each core and component idea with an essential question that frames the main concept. Each component idea also contains grade band "endpoints" for the end of grades 2, 5, 8, and 12.

Analysis
The *Framework* acknowledges that the content included in the first three physical science core ideas "parallel those identified in previous documents," including the *NSES* and *Benchmarks* (p. 5-1).

The authors introduce a fourth core idea, Waves and Their Applications in Technologies for Information Transfer, which "introduces students to the ways in which advances in the physical sciences during the 20th century underlie all sophisticated technologies today." In addition, the *Framework* acknowledges that "organizing science instruction around core disciplinary ideas tends to leave out the applications of those ideas" (p. 5-1). This core idea also provides an opportunity to stress the interplay between science and technology.

The endpoints, though not standards, will undoubtedly provide the disciplinary content that will form one of the three components in the performance standards called for in Recommendations 4 and 5 from Chapter 12.

Suggested Action

Review the *Framework* endpoints for the physical sciences and compare them with the topics or outcomes in your curriculum and assessment. In each of these content areas, we suggest educators keep an eye toward the vertical alignment of the content and check to see that there are no missing core ideas at each grade band. Keep in mind that some local topics/outcomes will not appear in the *Framework* since one of the charges to the writers was to "identify a small set of core ideas in each of the major science disciplines" (p. 1-11). Educators can anticipate finding additional content in their local curriculum, much of which can and should be eliminated as the curriculum is adjusted to meet the upcoming *NGSS*.

The inclusion of the fourth core idea will require some additions to the curriculum of most schools when the *NGSS* are released and adopted by states and schools. Instructional materials for this core idea may not be readily available for some time.

The suggested action section for Chapter 8 contains suggestions for thinking about where and how engineering core ideas can be integrated in the science curriculum.

Chapter 6
Dimension 3: Disciplinary Core Ideas: Life Sciences

Overview
The life sciences section has been organized under the following four core ideas and 14 component ideas.

Core Idea LS1: From Molecules to Organisms: Structures and Processes
- LS1.A: Structure and Function
- LS1.B: Growth and Development of Organisms
- LS1.C: Organization for Matter and Energy Flow in Organisms
- LS1.D: Information Processing

Core Idea LS2: Ecosystems: Interactions, Energy, and Dynamics
- LS2.A: Interdependent Relationships in Ecosystems
- LS2.B: Cycles of Matter and Energy Transfer in Ecosystems
- LS2.C: Ecosystem Dynamics, Functioning, and Resilience
- LS2.D: Social Interactions and Group Behavior

Core Idea LS3: Heredity: Inheritance and Variation of Traits
- LS3.A: Inheritance of Traits
- LS3.B: Variation of Traits

Core Idea LS4: Biological Evolution: Unity and Diversity
- LS4.A: Evidence of Common Ancestry and Diversity
- LS4.B: Natural Selection
- LS4.C: Adaptation
- LS4.D: Biodiversity and Humans

The *Framework* introduces each core and component idea with an essential question that frames the main concept. Each component idea also contains grade band endpoints for the end of grades 2, 5, 8, and 12.

Analysis
The *Framework* states that the four core ideas "have a long history and solid foundation based on the research evidence established by many scientists working across multiple fields" (p. 6-2). The ideas draw on those identified in previous documents, including the *NSES* and *Benchmarks*, as well as numerous reports from the National Research Council (NRC), American Association for the Advancement of Science (AAAS), National Assessment of Educational Progress (NAEP), Trends in International Mathematics and Science Study (TIMSS), College Board, and others.

Suggested Action

Review the *Framework* endpoints for the life sciences and compare them with the topics or outcomes in your school or district's curriculum. Keep in mind that some local topics/outcomes will not appear in the *Framework* since one of the charges to the writers was to "identify a small set of core ideas in each of the major science disciplines" (p. 1-11). Educators can anticipate finding additional content in their local curriculum, much of which can and should be eliminated as the curriculum is adjusted to meet the upcoming *NGSS*.

Be aware of the progression of the endpoints in each grade band. The *Framework* has been very attentive to the progression of ideas for each of the core ideas. The grade band or level may be different from your curriculum or from that of the *NSES* or *Benchmarks*.

Chapter 7
Dimension 3: Disciplinary Core Ideas:
Earth and Space Sciences

Overview
The Earth and space sciences section has been organized under the following three core ideas and 12 component ideas.

Core Idea ESS1: Earth's Place in the Universe
- ESS1.A: The Universe and Its Stars
- ESS1.B: Earth and the Solar System
- ESS1.C: The History of Planet Earth

Core Idea ESS2: Earth's Systems
- ESS2.A: Earth Materials and Systems
- ESS2.B: Plate Tectonics and Large-Scale System Interactions
- ESS2.C: The Roles of Water in Earth's Surface Processes
- ESS2.D: Weather and Climate
- ESS2.E: Biogeology

Core Idea ESS3: Earth and Human Activity
- ESS3.A: Natural Resources
- ESS3.B: Natural Hazards
- ESS3.C: Human Impacts on Earth Systems
- ESS3.D: Global Climate Change

Analysis
The *Framework* authors drew from several recent projects to delineate the Earth and space sciences content, including *Earth Science Literacy Principles: The Big Ideas and Supporting Concepts of Earth Science* (Earth Science Literacy Initiative 2010), *Ocean Literacy: The Essential Principles of Ocean Science K–12* (NGS 2006), *Essential Principles and Fundamental Concepts for Atmospheric Science Literacy* (UCAR 2008), and *Climate Literacy: The Essential Principles of Climate Science* (U.S. Global Change Research Program 2009). The core ideas include a broader range of content than most previous standards documents, but fewer outcomes. The increased breadth is especially evident in the third core idea, Earth and Human Activity, which deals with the increased stress on the planet and its resources due to rapidly increasing population and global industrialization.

Although the core ideas of Earth and space science cover a broader range of ideas, when compared to most Earth and space science instructional materials, the number of topics (components) has been reduced significantly in most areas and the topic of human impact has been more significantly stressed. This shift will ultimately place a burden on teachers and curriculum specialists to modify their curriculum and course syllabi.

Suggested Action

Begin the process of comparing your local curriculum to the endpoints for Earth and Space Sciences in the *Framework*. You may find that your curriculum or instructional materials have more topics and more detailed information or concepts than those outlined in the *Framework*. The opposite may be true for the third core idea, Earth and Human Activity, which describes how Earth's processes and human activity affect each other. Be aware of the progression of the endpoints in each grade band. The *Framework* has been very attentive to the progression of ideas for each of the core ideas. Local examples and illustrations of Earth science core ideas are excellent teaching resources. Begin to catalog them for use in the current curriculum or the revised curriculum, as it will help implement the *NGSS*.

Chapter 8
Dimension 3: Disciplinary Core Ideas: Engineering, Technology, and Applications of Science

Overview
The engineering, technology, and applications of sciences section has been organized under the following two core ideas and five component ideas.

Core Idea ETS1: Engineering Design
- ETS1.A: Defining and Delimiting an Engineering Problem
- ETS1.B: Developing Possible Solutions
- ETS1.C: Optimizing the Design Solution

Core Idea ETS2: Links Among Engineering, Technology, Science, and Society
- ETS2.A: Interdependence of Science, Engineering, and Technology
- ETS2.B: Influence of Engineering, Technology, and Science on Society and the Natural World

Analysis
While the intent of this chapter is to help students learn how science is used through the engineering design process, the two core ideas have different goals. The goal of the first idea is to help students develop an understanding of engineering design, while the second is to help them make connections among engineering, technology, and science. Although the *language* defining the process of engineering design may be new to science educators, the *ideas* are not new for many of them, particularly those at the elementary level and those using project activities in their teaching. For example, students designing and building a structure in an elementary science unit have followed the three procedures described in the Core Idea ETS1, possibly without the explicit understanding of the engineering design process and use of the terminology.

The early paragraphs in this chapter provide the essential, but limited, direction that learning engineering requires, combining the engineering practices outlined in Chapter 3 with the understanding of engineering design contained in Chapter 8 in the same way that science involves both knowledge and a set of practices.

The second core idea is an excellent complement to the engineering core ideas taught in the science curriculum since it brings together the interdependence of engineering, technology, science, and society. Readers familiar with the standards for Science in Personal and Societal Perspectives in the *NSES* will see some overlap with the core ideas in this section of the *Framework*.

The core ideas in this chapter and those in Chapter 3 dealing with engineering practices may prove to be a significant shift for science educators when the *NGSS* appear. Although many teachers and instructional materials rely on activities that are engineering in nature, the language and specific outcome described in Core Ideas ETS1 and ETS2 are not normally included as part of the activities. A paradigm shift is called for that might be approached with the following professional development activities and curriculum development work.

Suggested Action

Form study or discussion groups to read and discuss the nature of engineering using resources such as the National Academy of Engineering publication *Standards for K–12 Engineering Education?* (NRC 2010b). This and many other reports can be downloaded for free at *www.nap.edu*.

Study the definitions in Box 8-1, "Definitions of Technology, Engineering, and Applications of Science" (p. 8-11), at the end of the chapter to help gain clarity on the distinction between engineering and technology. Notice the connection between the two definitions. An excellent book on the nature of technology is *The Nature of Technology: What It Is and How It Evolves* (Arthur 2009).

Assemble a team to begin assessing how and where engineering core ideas might be integrated in the science curriculum at each grade band in your school or district. Some courses or units lend themselves to this integration better than others. What are they? Do new activities or units need to be added? Can some of the existing activities be modified or supplemented to provide outcomes in engineering? Where and how can the endpoints from the practices of engineering and the core ideas in this chapter be combined as parallel outcomes of modified or new activities?

Identify or plan professional development activities to immerse teachers in doing engineering design projects and gaining knowledge of the language and endpoints expected of their students. Keep in mind that a thorough modification and revision of instructional material should wait until the new standards are reasonably complete and available.

PART III:
Realizing the Vision

Chapter 9
Integrating the Three Dimensions

Overview
This chapter describes the process of integrating the three dimensions (practices, crosscutting concepts, and core ideas) in the *NGSS* and provides two examples for its writers, as well as for the writers of instructional materials and assessments. The preceding chapters described the dimensions separately to provide a clear understanding of each; this chapter recognizes the need and value of integrating them in standards and instruction. The *Framework* is specific about this task as indicated by the following statement (p. 9-1): "A major task for developers will be to create standards that integrate the three dimensions. The committee suggests that this integration should occur in the standards statements themselves and in performance expectations that link to the standards."

This expectation is based on the assumption that "students cannot fully understand scientific and engineering ideas without engaging in the practices of inquiry and the discourses by which such ideas are developed and refined. ... At the same time, they cannot learn or show competence in practices except in the context of specific content" (p. 9-1).

Performance expectations are a necessary and essential component of the standard statements. These expectations describe how students will demonstrate an understanding and application of the core ideas. The chapter provides two illustrations in Table 9-1, "Sample Performance Expectations in the Life Sciences" (p. 9-12), and Table 9-2, "Sample Performance Expectations in the Physical Sciences" (p. 9-16), of what the performance expectation could look like for two core ideas.

Although it is not the function of the *Framework* or the *NGSS* to provide detailed descriptions of instruction, this *Framework* chapter offers a fairly extensive example—in narrative form—of what the integration of the three dimensions for a physical science core idea at each grade band (K–2, 3–5, 6–8, and 9–12) would look like. One of the unique features of this example is the inclusion of "boundary statements" that specify ideas that do *not* need to be included. The standard statements are expected to contain boundary statements.

Analysis
Although Tables 9-1 and 9-2 are extensive examples of performance expectation for two core ideas, they are not a model for the format of the standards statements that will appear in the *NGSS*. The practices and crosscutting concepts are only identified and not spelled out in performance language. We will not know the actual format and structure of the standards that integrate the three dimensions until the first draft is released, and we will not know specifics of the final standards until sometime later. The new integrated standards will be a significant

departure from those in the previous national standards documents, and they will have a huge impact on instruction, instructional materials, and assessments for science educators.

There are few, if any, examples or precedents for this type of standard. Such standards may very well prescribe the instruction and assessment that should be included in the curriculum and instructional materials. Performance expectations indicate the core idea, the practice that should be used or at least emphasized, and the crosscutting concepts that should be included. The performance for each of the dimensions comes close to describing how each should be assessed. The detailed instructional strategies and instructional materials will be left to the instructor, but the outcomes suggested by the practices will be determined by the standard statements and the associated performance expectations.

Suggested Action

The development of instructional materials, their implementation, and the associated assessment from integrated standards will be the second major shift (after the inclusion of engineering) that appears in the *NGSS*. We recommend the following general strategies to accommodate this shift:

- Conduct extensive reading, form study groups, and explore other professional development avenues to become deeply familiar with the scientific and engineering practices, the crosscutting concepts, and the core ideas in the *Framework*. The integration of the dimensions will be most effective if educators have a thorough and clear understanding of each dimension.
- Study Tables 9-1 and 9-2 and the narrative example of instruction from the physical sciences.
- Begin searching for instructional materials that explicitly integrate the three dimensions. Examples may begin to appear in professional literature such as NSTA journals. Examine and evaluate them carefully.
- When the first draft of the *NGSS* appears, study carefully the content of a standard statement at your grade band. As a learning exercise, assemble a small team of colleagues and sketch out a series of lessons or a small unit to facilitate a group of students meeting the performance expectations in the standard. This exercise is only a sample of what will be required to meet the new performance expectations, but it will assist in your planning of longer-range activities and projects when the final version of the *NGSS* is published and adopted by your state or school district.

Chapter 10
Implementation: Curriculum Instruction, Teacher Development, and Assessment

Overview

Most readers will recall that the *NSES* include standards for the components of teaching, professional development, assessment, educational programs, and educational systems. This chapter acknowledges the value of those standards and the fact that the charge to the *Framework* developers did not include a similar comprehensive assignment to provide standards or even recommendations. This chapter assumes the task of analyzing the overall education system and discusses "what must be in place in order for [each component] to align with the framework's vision" (p. 10-1). In doing so, it depends heavily on a number of recent reports from the NRC that reviewed the research related to each component in the *Framework*. These include *Knowing What Students Know* (Pellegrino, Chudowsky, and Glaser 2001), *Investigating the Influence of Standards* (Weiss et al. 2002), *Systems for State Science Assessments* (Wilson and Bertenthal 2006), *America's Lab Report* (Singer, Hilton, and Schweingruber 2006), *Taking Science to School* (Duschl, Schweingruber, and Shouse 2007), and *Preparing Teachers* (NRC 2010a).

After briefly describing the total education system and calling for coherence within it, the *Framework* addresses the components of curriculum and instruction, teacher development, and assessment.

The section on curriculum and instruction lists a variety of "aspects for curriculum designers to consider that are not addressed in the framework ... that the committee considers important but decided would be better treated at the level of curriculum design than at the level of framework and standards" (p. 10-5). These include the historical, cultural, and ethical aspects of science and its applications, and the history of scientific and engineering ideas and the individual practitioners.

Analysis

For many experienced science educators, this section of the *Framework* is the most important despite its limited treatment. The missing ingredient in the first release of the *NSES* and *Benchmarks* was the lack of extensive implementation at the state and local level. Both the *NSES* and the *Benchmarks* received a great deal of attention and some replication in state standards, but the standards for teaching, professional development, assessment, program, and systems did not receive equal emphasis. NSTA believes that for new standards to be implemented successfully, a significant emphasis must be placed on outreach and support for science educators.

The section in the *Framework* on instruction does not go into great depth on the topic and defers to the extensive discussion of the topic and the research behind it in *Taking Science to School* (Duschl, Schweingruber, and Shouse 2007). Teacher development and assessment sections are also light and depend on existing NRC reports previously listed in the overview section.

Suggested Action

The call to integrate the practices, crosscutting concepts, and the core ideas will require a new and greater emphasis on incorporating change in all components of the system. The *NGSS* are what is to be implemented, not the *Framework*, but the task of implementation needs to start now, long before the *NGSS* are published and adopted in states and school districts. It is not the role of this guide to spell out the multiple steps and decisions that need to be made to implement a new set of standards, but that process needs to begin now! The starting points have been outlined in the previous sections.

To stay informed, follow the NSTA *NGSS* website (*www.nsta.org/ngss*), which provides a continuous flow of information about the draft versions of *NGSS* as they are released.

Chapter 11
Equity and Diversity in Science and Engineering Education

Overview

This chapter highlights the issues in achieving equity in education opportunities for all students, summarizes the research on the lack of equity in education in general and science education in particular, describes what should be available for all students in broad strokes, and makes a limited number of specific recommendations to the standards developers. The discussion of inequity of education achievement among specific demographic groups is reduced to two key areas: (1) the differences in the opportunity to learn due to inequities in schools and communities; and (2) the lack of inclusiveness in instruction to motivate diverse student populations. The research is clear that all students, with rare exceptions, have the capacity to learn complex subject matter when support is available over an extended period of time.

The *Framework* recommends that the *NGSS* (1) specify that rigorous learning goals (standards) are appropriate for all students and (2) make explicit the need for the instructional time, facilities, and teacher knowledge that can help all students achieve these goals.

On a more general but no less significant level, the *Framework* recommendations address the need to equalize the opportunity to learn. This means providing inclusive science instruction, making diversity visible, and providing multiple modes of expression. To make science instruction more inclusive, the *Framework* suggests several strategies: approaching science learning as a cultural accomplishment, relating youth discourses to scientific discourses, building on prior interest and identity, and leveraging students' cultural funds of knowledge.

The final recommendation in the chapter focuses on creating assessments that use multiple opportunities for students to express their understanding of the content in multiple contexts and avoiding culturally biased assessment instruments.

Analysis

The *Framework* gives the critical issue of equity and diversity modest attention, but it provides a number of well-researched recommendations. Most of the recommendations in the chapter focus on instruction and cultural contexts of education more than the nature of standards. The limited attention to these issues in the *Framework*, due to the charge to the committee of writers, should in no way detract from its extreme importance.

Suggested Action

Schools should reexamine their progress with equity and diversity and reshape their efforts based on the specific recommendations provided in the *Framework*. There is no need to wait to address these issues until the *NGSS* are released; the issues of equity and diversity should be an ongoing agenda for all schools and teachers, and should be addressed aggressively and consistently.

Chapter 12
Guidance for Standards Developers

Overview

This chapter opens with the recommendation from *Systems for State Science Assessments* (Wilson and Bertenthal 2006) that standards should be "clear, detailed, and complete; reasonable in scope; rigorously and scientifically correct, and based on sound models of student learning … [and] should have a clear conceptual framework, describe performance expectations, and identify proficiency levels" (p. 12-1).

It then lists the following 13 specific recommendations for standard developers with a short discussion following each recommendation. (These recommendations are quoted directly from the *Framework*.)

1. Standards should set rigorous learning goals that represent a common expectation for all students (p. 12-2).
2. Standards should be scientifically accurate yet also clear, concise, and comprehensible to science educators (p. 12-2).
3. Standards should be limited in number (p. 12-3).
4. Standards should emphasize all three dimensions articulated in the framework—not only crosscutting concepts and disciplinary core ideas but also scientific and engineering practices (p. 12-3).
5. Standards should include performance expectations that integrate the scientific and engineering practices with the crosscutting concepts and disciplinary core ideas. These expectations should include criteria for identifying successful performance and require that students demonstrate an ability to use and apply knowledge (p. 12-4).
6. Standards should incorporate boundary statements. That is, for a given core idea at a given grade level, standards developers should include guidance not only about what needs to be taught but also about what does ***not*** need to be taught in order for students to achieve the standard (p. 12-4).
7. Standards should be organized as sequences that support students' learning over multiple grades. They should take into account how students' command of the practices, concepts, and core ideas becomes more sophisticated over time with appropriate instructional experiences (p. 12-5).
8. Whenever possible, the progressions in standards should be informed by existing research on learning and teaching. In cases in which insufficient research is available to inform a progression or in which there is a lack of consensus on the research findings, the progression should be developed on the basis of a reasoned argument about learning and teaching. The sequences described in the framework can be used as guidance (p. 12-5).
9. The committee recommends that the diverse needs of students and of states be met by developing grade band standards as an overarching common set for adoption by mul-

tiple states. For those states that prefer or require grade-by-grade standards, a suggested elaboration on grade band standards could be provided as an example (p. 12-6).

10. If grade-by-grade standards are written based on the grade band descriptions provided in the framework, these standards should be designed to provide a coherent progression within each grade band (p. 12-7).

11. Any assumptions about the resources, time, and teacher expertise needed for students to achieve particular standards should be made explicit (p. 12-7).

12. The standards for the sciences and engineering should align coherently with those for other K–12 subjects. Alignment with the Common Core Standards in mathematics and English/language arts is especially important (p. 12-7).

13. In designing standards and performance expectations, issues related to diversity and equity need to be taken into account. In particular, performance expectations should provide students with multiple ways of demonstrating competence in science (p. 12-8).

Analysis

Although specifically addressed to Achieve Inc., the group writing the *NGSS*, the recommendations provide a preview of what to expect in the standards document. The reader will notice that the 13 recommendations are closely aligned with the content of the first 11 chapters.

Suggested Action

A few states and districts may be developing their own standards independent of the work being undertaken by Achieve Inc. To those few, the recommendations are germane and highly relevant. To the majority of readers, they are predictors of what to expect in the first and subsequent drafts of the *NGSS*. In most cases, more attention should be paid to the previous sections where the issues that give rise to the recommendations are well articulated.

Chapter 13
Looking Toward the Future:
Research and Development to Inform
K–12 Science Education Standards

Overview

Chapter 13 reminds the reader that the *Framework* is based on research and lays out the research agenda for the next near term (five to seven years) and the long term (seven years and beyond). The recommended agenda can be summarized with the following outline, which lists two major areas of research with a number of issues or questions under each.

I. Research to Inform Implementation and Future Revisions of the *Framework*
    A. Learning and Instruction
        1. What are the typical preconceptions that students hold about the practices, cross-cutting concepts, and core ideas at the outset?
        2. What is the expected progression of understanding, and what are the predictable points of difficulty that must be overcome?
        3. What instructional interventions (e.g., curriculum materials, teaching practices, simulations or other technology tools, instructional activities) can move students along a path from their initial understanding to the desired outcome?
        4. What general and discipline-specific norms and instructional practices best engage and support student learning?
        5. How can students of both genders and of all cultural backgrounds, languages, and abilities become engaged in the instructional activities needed to move toward more sophisticated understanding?
        6. How can the individual student's understanding and progress be monitored? (p. 13-2)
    B. Learning Progressions
    C. Scientific and Engineering Practices
    D. Development of Curricular and Instructional Materials
    E. Assessment
    F. Supporting Teachers' Learning

II. Understanding the Impact of the *Framework* and Related Standards
    A. Curriculum and Instructional Materials
    B. Teacher and Administrator Development
    C. Assessment and Accountability
    D. Organizational Issues

Analysis

Throughout the *Framework*, the reader is reminded that the document is based on a considerable body of solid education research, which is cited frequently. It should be pointed out that the National Research Council does not do original research; it reviews and evaluates the research already completed by others. The NRC is a part of the National Academies, a private nonprofit institution that provides expert advice on some of the most pressing challenges facing the nation and the world through the publication of reports that have helped shape sound policies; inform public opinion; and advance the pursuit of science, engineering, and medicine. Several new documents are cited in this chapter, including *Learning and Instruction: A SERP (Strategic Education Research Partnership) Research Agenda* (Donovan and Pellegrino 2004), which influenced the agenda and research question on learning and instruction in the *Framework*. The questions in the report could lead to and shape local school district or university cooperative research activities.

Suggested Action

Motivated readers may want to acquire and study the various research reports from the NRC that have been cited in the earlier chapters. As the standards are released and adoption and implementation begin, the question of why many of the changes or shifts from the previous documents and recommendations for classroom practices were made will be asked. The background research can be useful in making local and state decisions for curriculum and assessment and defending them in public and legislative settings.

The suggested action items in the previous chapters provide a host of ideas for science educators and others to gain a deep understanding of the *Framework* as a stand-alone document and as a guide to the use of the forthcoming *NGSS*. We encourage you to pursue these and other opportunities with colleagues to better prepare for the new standards.

Harold Pratt, a former NSTA president, served as senior program officer at the National Research Council, where he helped develop the National Science Education Standards. He has also worked as executive director of curriculum for the Jefferson County Public Schools in Colorado and project director at BSCS. He has authored and published numerous books, chapters, and articles.

References

American Association for the Advancement of Science (AAAS). 1993. *Benchmarks for science literacy.* New York: Oxford University Press.

Arthur, W. B. 2009. *The nature of technology: What it is and how it evolves.* New York: Free Press.

Bell, P., B. Lewenstein, A. W. Shouse, and M. A. Feder, eds. 2009. *Learning science in informal environments: People, places, and pursuits.* Washington, DC: National Academies Press.

Bransford, J. D., A. L. Brown, and R. J. Cocking, eds. 2000. *How people learn: Brain, mind, experience, and school.* Washington, DC: National Academies Press.

Donovan, M. S., and J. W. Pellegrino 2004. *Learning and instruction: A SERP (Strategic Education Research Partnership) research agenda.* Washington, DC: National Academies Press.

Duschl, R. A., H. A. Schweingruber, and A. W. Shouse, eds. 2007. *Taking science to school: Learning and teaching science in grades K–8.* Washington, DC: National Academies Press.

Earth Science Literacy Initiative. 2010. *Earth science literacy principles: The big ideas and supporting concepts of Earth science.* Arlington, VA: National Science Foundation. *www.earthscienceliteracy.org/ es_literacy_6may10_.pdf*

Katehi, L., G. Pearson, and M. Feders, eds. 2009. *Engineering in K–12 education: Understanding the status and improving the prospects.* Washington, DC: National Academies Press.

Michaels, S., A. W. Shouse, and H. A. Schweingruber, eds. 2008. *Ready, set, science! Putting research to work in K–8 science classrooms.* Washington, DC: National Academies Press.

National Geographic Society (NGS). 2006. *Ocean literacy: The essential principles of ocean science K–12.* Washington, DC: NGS. *www.coexploration.org/oceanliteracy/documents/OceanLitChart.pdf*

National Research Council (NRC). 1996. *National science education standards.* Washington, DC: National Academies Press.

National Research Council (NRC). 2010a. *Preparing teachers: Building evidence for sound policy.* Washington, DC: National Academies Press.

National Research Council (NRC). 2010b. *Standards for K–12 engineering education?* Washington, DC: National Academies Press.

National Research Council (NRC). 2011. *A Framework for K–12 Science Education: Practices, Crosscutting Concepts, and Core Ideas.* Washington, DC: National Academies Press.

Pellegrino, J. W., N. Chudowsky, and R. Glaser, eds. 2001. *Knowing what students know: The science and design of education assessment.* Washington, DC: National Academies Press.

Singer, S. R., M. L. Hilton, and H. A. Schweingruber, eds. 2006. *America's lab report: Investigations in high school science.* Washington, DC: National Academies Press.

University Corporation for Atmospheric Research (UCAR). 2008. *Essential principles and fundamental concepts for atmospheric science literacy.* Boulder, CO: UCAR. *http://eo.ucar.edu/asl/pdfs/ ASLbrochureFINAL.pdf*

U.S. Global Change Research Program/Climate Change Science Program. 2009. *Climate literacy: The essential principles of climate science.* Washington, DC: U.S. Global Change Research Program/ Climate Change Science Program. *www.climatescience.gov/Library/Literacy/default.php*

Weiss I. R., M. S. Knapp, K. S. Hollweg, and G. Burrill, eds. 2002. *Investigating the influence of standards: A framework for research in mathematics, science, and technology education.* Washington, DC: National Academies Press.

Wilson, M. R., and M. W. Bertenthal, eds. 2006. *Systems for state science assessments.* Washington, DC: National Academies Press.

Understanding
A FRAMEWORK FOR
K–12 SCIENCE
EDUCATION

Practices, Crosscutting Concepts, and Core Ideas

Top Science Educators Offer Insight

Scientific and Engineering Practices in K–12 Classrooms

By Rodger W. Bybee

This morning I watched *Sesame Street*. During the show, characters "acted like engineers" and designed a boat so a rock could float. In another segment, children asked questions and made predictions about the best design for a simple car. They then built a model car and completed an investigation to determine which design worked best when the cars went down inclined planes. Children also learned that a wider base provided stability for a tower. And, among other segments, the children counted from 1 to 12 and explored the different combinations of numbers that equaled 12. Bert and Ernie had to move a rock and ended up "inventing" a wheel. These segments exemplify the science, technology, engineering, and mathematics (STEM) theme that *Sesame Street* is introducing in the show's 42nd season.

What, you ask, does this have to do with science and engineering practices in K–12 classrooms? The producers of *Sesame Street* decided that STEM practices were important enough that they are using them as substantive themes for the season, if not longer. Children watching *Sesame Street* will have been introduced to practices such as asking questions and defining problems; developing and using models; planning and carrying out investigations; analyzing and interpreting data; using mathematics; constructing explanations and designing solutions; engaging in arguments using evidence; and obtaining, evaluating, and communicating information. True, these are sophisticated statements of practices, but many students will be introduced to them when they enter elementary classrooms.

Here, I present the science and engineering practices from the recently released *A Framework for K–12 Science Education: Practices, Crosscutting Concepts, and Core Ideas* (NRC 2011). I recognize the changes implied by the new framework, and eventually a new generation of science education standards will present new perspectives for the science education community. I am especially sensitive to the challenges for those students in teacher preparation programs and classroom teachers of science at all levels. Questions such as "Why practices and why not inquiry?" and "Why science *and* engineering?" are reasonable, and I will discuss them later. But to provide background and context, I first discuss the practices.

Understanding and applying the science and engineering practices

This section further elaborates on the practices and briefly describes what students are to know and be able to do, and how they might be taught. Figures 1 through 8 are adapted from the National Research Council (NRC) *Framework*, with changes for clarity and balance. I have maintained the substantive content.

Even before elementary school, children ask questions of each other and of adults about things around them, including the natural and designed world. If students develop the practices of science and engineering, they can ask better questions and improve how they define problems. Students should, for example, learn how to ask questions of each other, to recognize the difference between questions and problems, and to evaluate scientific questions and engineering problems from other types of questions. In upper grades, the practices of asking scientific questions and defining engineering problems advance in subtle ways such as the form and function of data used in answering questions and the criteria and constraints applied to solving problems.

In the lower grades, the idea of scientific and engineering models can be introduced using pictures, diagrams, drawings, and simple physical models such as airplanes or cars. In upper grades, simulations and more sophisticated conceptual, mathematical, and computational models may be used to conduct investigations, explore changes in system components, and generate data that can be used in formulating scientific explanations or in proposing technological solutions.

Planning and carrying out investigations should be standard experiences in K–12 classrooms. Across the grades students develop deeper and richer understandings and abilities as they conduct different types of investigations, use different technologies to collect data, give greater attention to the types of variables, and clarify the scientific and/or engineering contexts for investigations.

Figure 1. Asking questions and defining problems

Science begins with a question about a phenomenon such as "Why is the sky blue?" or "What causes cancer?" A basic practice of the scientist is the ability to formulate empirically answerable questions about phenomena to establish what is already known, and to determine what questions have yet to be satisfactorily answered.	**Engineering** begins with a problem that needs to be solved, such as "How can we reduce the nation's dependence on fossil fuels?" or "What can be done to reduce a particular disease?" or "How can we improve the fuel efficiency of automobiles?" A basic practice of engineers is to ask questions to clarify the problem, determine criteria for a successful solution, and identify constraints.

Figure 2. Developing and using models

Science often involves the construction and use of models and simulations to help develop explanations about natural phenomena. Models make it possible to go beyond observables and simulate a world not yet seen. Models enable predictions of the form "if…then…therefore" to be made in order to test hypothetical explanations.	**Engineering** makes use of models and simulations to analyze extant systems to identify flaws that might occur, or to test possible solutions to a new problem. Engineers design and use models of various sorts to test proposed systems and to recognize the strengths and limitations of their designs.

Figure 3. Planning and carrying out investigations

Scientific investigations may be conducted in the field or in the laboratory. A major practice of scientists is planning and carrying out systematic investigations that require clarifying what counts as data and in experiments identifying variables.	**Engineering investigations** are conducted to gain data essential for specifying criteria or parameters and to test proposed designs. Like scientists, engineers must identify relevant variables, decide how they will be measured, and collect data for analysis. Their investigations help them to identify the effectiveness, efficiency, and durability of designs under different conditions.

Both science and engineering involve the analysis and interpretation of data. In lower grades, students simply record and share observations though drawings, writing, whole numbers, and oral reports. In middle and high school, students report relationships and patterns in data, distinguish between correlation and causation, and compare and contrast independent sets of data for consistency and confirmation of an explanation or solution.

The overlap of these practices with the next practices, using mathematical and computational thinking, is significant. Although both of these sets of practices can be completed with simulated data, it is beneficial for students to actually experience the practices of collecting, analyzing, and interpreting data and in the process apply mathematical and computational thinking.

In the early grades, students can learn to use appropriate instruments (e.g., rulers and thermometers) and their units in measurements and in quantitative results to compare proposed solutions to an engineering problem. In upper grades, students can use computers to analyze data sets and express the significance of data using statistics.

Students can learn to use computers to record measurements, summarize and display data, and calculate relationships. As students progress to higher grades, their experiences in science classes should enhance what they learn in math class.

The aim for students at all grade levels is to learn how to use evidence to formulate a logically coherent explanation of phenomena and to support a proposed solution for an engineering problem. The construction of an explanation or solution should incorporate current

Figure 4. Analyzing and interpreting data

Scientific investigations produce data that must be analyzed in order to derive meaning. Because data usually do not speak for themselves, scientists use a range of tools—including tabulation, graphical interpretation, visualization, and statistical analysis—to identify the significant features and patterns in the data. Sources of error are identified and the degree of certainty calculated. Modern technology makes the collection of large data sets much easier providing secondary sources for analysis.	**Engineering investigations** include analysis of data collected in the tests of designs. This allows comparison of different solutions and determines how well each meets specific design criteria—that is, which design best solves the problem within given constraints. Like scientists, the engineers require a range of tools to identify the major patterns and interpret the results. Advances in science make analysis of proposed solutions more efficient and effective.

Figure 5. Using mathematics and computational thinking

In **science,** mathematics and computation are fundamental tools for representing physical variables and their relationships. They are used for a range of tasks such as constructing simulations; statistically analyzing data; and recognizing, expressing, and applying quantitative relationships. Mathematical and computational approaches enable prediction of the behavior of physical systems along with the testing of such predictions. Moreover, statistical techniques are also invaluable for identifying significant patterns and establishing correlational relationships.	In **engineering,** mathematical and computational representations of established relationships and principles are an integral part of the design process. For example, structural engineers create mathematical-based analysis of designs to calculate whether they can stand up to expected stresses of use and if they can be completed within acceptable budgets. Moreover, simulations provide an effective test bed for the development of designs as proposed solutions to problems and their improvement, if required.

scientific knowledge and often include a model. These practices along with those in Figure 1 differentiate science from engineering.

In elementary grades, students might listen to two different explanations for an observation and decide which is better supported with evidence. Students might listen to other students' proposed solutions and ask for the evidence supporting the proposal. In upper grades, students should learn to identify claims; differentiate between data and evidence; and use logical reasoning in oral, written, and graphic presentations.

Figure 6. Constructing explanations and designing solutions

The goal of **science** is the construction of theories that provide explanatory accounts of the material world. A theory becomes accepted when it has multiple independent lines of empirical evidence, greater explanatory power, a breadth of phenomena it accounts for, and has explanatory coherence and parsimony.	The goal of **engineering** design is a systematic solution to problems that is based on scientific knowledge and models of the material world. Each proposed solution results from a process of balancing competing criteria of desired functions, technical feasibility, cost, safety, aesthetics, and compliance with legal requirements. Usually there is no one best solution, but rather a range of solutions. The optimal choice depends on how well the proposed solution meets criteria and constraints.

Figure 7. Engaging in argument from evidence

In **science**, reasoning and argument are essential for clarifying strengths and weaknesses of a line of evidence and for identifying the best explanation for a natural phenomenon. Scientists must defend their explanations, formulate evidence based on a solid foundation of data, examine their understanding in light of the evidence and comments by others, and collaborate with peers in searching for the best explanation for the phenomena being investigated.	In **engineering**, reasoning and argument are essential for finding the best solution to a problem. Engineers collaborate with their peers throughout the design process. With a critical stage being the selection of the most promising solution among a field of competing ideas. Engineers use systematic methods to compare alternatives, formulate evidence based on test data, make arguments to defend their conclusions, critically evaluate the ideas of others, and revise their designs in order to identify the best solution.

Figure 8. Obtaining, evaluating, and communicating information

Science cannot advance if scientists are unable to communicate their findings clearly and persuasively or learn about the findings of others. A major practice of science is thus to communicate ideas and the results of inquiry—orally; in writing; with the use of tables, diagrams, graphs and equations; and by engaging in extended discussions with peers. Science requires the ability to derive meaning from scientific texts such as papers, the internet, symposia, or lectures to evaluate the scientific validity of the information thus acquired and to integrate that information into proposed explanations.	**Engineering** cannot produce new or improved technologies if the advantages of their designs are not communicated clearly and persuasively. Engineers need to be able to express their ideas orally and in writing; with the use of tables, graphs, drawings or models; and by engaging in extended discussions with peers. Moreover, as with scientists, they need to be able to derive meaning from colleagues' texts, evaluate information, and apply it usefully.

In elementary grades, these practices entail sharing scientific and technological information; mastering oral and written presentations; and appropriately using models, drawings, and numbers. As students progress, the practices become more complex and might include preparing reports of investigations; communicating using multiple formats; constructing arguments; and incorporating multiple lines of evidence, different models, and evaluative analysis.

With this introduction and overview of science and engineering practices, I turn to some of the questions engaged by a shift in teaching strategies and learning outcomes. Although science teachers have many questions, the next sections discuss two questions that seem prominent: "Why *practices*?" and "Why *engineering*?"

Why *practices*?

Science teachers have asked, "Why use the term *practices*? Why not continue using *inquiry*?" These are reasonable questions. A brief history will provide the context for an answer.

One major innovation in the 1960s reform movement was the introduction of the *processes* of science as a replacement for the *methods* of science. The processes of science shifted the emphasis from students' memorizing five steps in the scientific method to learning specific and fundamental processes such as observing, clarifying, measuring, inferring, and predicting. To complement this new emphasis, the new reformed instructional materials incorporated activities, laboratories, and investigations that gave students opportunities to learn the processes of science while developing an understanding of the conceptual structure of science disciplines.

During the period 1960–1990, interest and support grew for *scientific inquiry* as an approach to science teaching that emphasized learning science concepts and using the skills and abilities of inquiry to learn those concepts.

This change toward scientific inquiry was expressed by leaders such as Joseph Schwab and Paul Brandwein and publications such as *Science for All Americans* (Rutherford and Ahlgren 1989). In the 1990s, scientific inquiry was fundamental to the *Benchmarks for Science Literacy* (AAAS 1993) and the *National Science Education Standards* (NRC 1996). Along with *Inquiry and the National Science Education Standards* (NRC 2000), these two publications had a significant influence on state standards and the place of inquiry in school science programs. It is important that scientific inquiry expanded and improved the earlier processes of science and provided richer understanding of science, a set of cognitive abilities for students, and more effective teaching strategies. One should note that the reforms toward the *processes of science* and *scientific inquiry* did result in greater emphasis on the use of activities and investigations as teaching strategies to learn science concepts. However, scientific inquiry has not been implemented as widely as expected.

During the 15 years since the release of the standards, researchers have advanced our knowledge about how students learn science (Bybee 2002; Donovan and Bransford 2005) and the way science functions. Advances in these and other areas have been synthesized in *Taking Science to School* (Duschl, Schweingruber, and Shouse 2007) and *Ready, Set, Science!* (Michaels, Shouse, and Schweingruber 2008). These two publications had a significant influence on the *Framework*.

Taking Science to School describes four proficiencies that link the content and practices of science. "Students who are proficient in science," the authors write,

- *know, use, and interpret scientific explanations of the natural world;*
- *generate and evaluate scientific evidence and explanations;*
- *understand the nature and development of scientific knowledge; and*
- *participate productively in scientific practices and discourse.* (Duschl, Schweingruber, and Shouse 2007, p. 2)

The following quote from *Ready, Set, Science!* builds on these proficiencies and presents an answer to the question, "Why practices?"

Throughout this book, we talk about "scientific practices" and refer to the kind of teaching that integrates the four strands as "science as practice." Why not use the term "inquiry" instead? Science practice involves doing something and learning something in such a way that the doing and learning cannot really be separated. Thus, "practice" . . . encompasses several of the different dictionary definitions of the term. It refers to doing something repeatedly in order to become proficient (as in practicing the trumpet). It refers to learning something so thoroughly that it becomes second nature (as in practicing thrift). And it refers to using one's knowledge to meet an objective (as in practicing law or practicing teaching). (Michaels, Shouse, and Schweingruber 2008, p. 34)

Scientific inquiry is one form of scientific practice. So, the perspective presented in the *Framework* is not one of replacing inquiry; rather, it is one of expanding and enriching the teaching and learning of science. Notice the emphasis on teaching strategies aligned with science practices. When students engage in scientific practices, activities become the basis for learning about experiments, data and evidence, social discourse, models and tools, and mathematics and for developing the ability to evaluate knowledge claims, conduct empirical investigations, and develop explanations.

Why *engineering?*

Again, a brief history establishes a context for the inclusion of engineering practices. In the 1960s, technology and engineering were marginalized in the U.S. science curriculum (Rudolph 2002). This said, the era of curriculum reform in the United States did produce one program, *The Man Made World*, developed by the Engineering Concepts Curriculum Project (1971). However, technology was included in other countries (Black and Atkin 1996; Atkin and Black 2003). Publication of *Science for All Americans* (Rutherford and Ahlgren 1989) included chapters on "the nature of technology" and "the Designed World." This reintroduction of technology and engineering was further advanced by their inclusion in the *Benchmarks for Science Literacy* (AAAS 1993) and *National Science Education Standards* (NRC 1996). Technology gained further support with the publication of the *Standards for Technological Literacy* (ITEA 2000).

In the early 21st century, the acronym STEM has emerged as a description of many and diverse educational initiatives. The *T* and *E* in STEM represent *technology* and *engineering*.

As the reader no doubt recognized in the eight figures, the practices of science and engineering overlap in many ways. With the exception of their goals—science proposes questions about the natural world and proposes answers in the form of evidence-based explanations, and engineering identifies problems of human needs and aspirations and proposes solutions in the form of new products and processes—science and engineering practices are parallel and complementary.

So, there is a need for science teachers and those in teacher education programs to recognize the similarities and differences between science and technology as disciplines and subsequently the practices that characterize the disciplines.

At elementary levels, there is good news. Many activities that are already in the curriculum are based on engineering problems. Building bridges, dropping eggs, and (as we saw in the opening on *Sesame Street*) designing model cars are all examples of engineering in elementary school programs. Unfortunately, these engineering problems and subsequent practices are often referred to erroneously as science. With a clarification of terms and a continuation of the activities, elementary teachers can introduce science and engineering practices without significant additions to the curriculum. And, as value added, the engineering problems are highly motivating for the students at all grade levels.

At the middle and high school levels, science teachers can begin with the technologies already used—microscopes, telescopes, and computers—as examples of the relationship between science and technology. In addition, there are examples clearly embedded in the practices of science and engineering. Here, I would also add the value of the history of science to show the role of technology and engineering and their contributions to the advance of scientific knowledge. An excellent contemporary example of the advance of science that is due to technology and engineering is the Hubble Space Telescope and its potential successor, the James Webb Space Telescope.

Complementing goals

This article explores one aspect of the new NRC *Framework*—science and engineering practices—in greater depth. Although the NRC report is a framework and not standards, it is prudent for those in the science and technology education community to begin preparing for the new standards.

Because science and engineering practices are basic to science education and the change from inquiry to practices is central, this innovation for the new standards will likely be one of the most significant challenges for the successful implementation of science education standards. The brief discussion that follows is based on the prior description of science and engineering practices in Figures 1 through 8.

The relationship between science and engineering practices is one of complementarity. Given the inclusion of engineering in the science standards and an understanding of the difference in aims, the practices complement one another and should be mutually reinforcing in curricula and instruction.

The shift to practices emerges from research on how students learn and advances our understanding of how science progresses. The new emphasis on practices includes scientific inquiry and goes beyond what science teachers have realized based on the 1990s standards. Indeed, as I have noted, there is overlap with the 1996 standards, for example.

The new emphasis on practices reinforces the need for school science programs to actively involve students through investigations and, in the 21st century, digitally based programs and activities. Hands-on and laboratory work should still contribute to the realization of practices in science classrooms. As we saw in the earlier quote from *Ready, Set, Science!,* there is a reasonable assumption that across the K–12 continuum the abilities and understandings of science and engineering practices will progressively get deeper and broader.

Science and engineering practices should be thought of as both learning outcomes and instructional strategies. They represent both educational ends and instructional means. First, students should develop the abilities described in the practices, and they should understand how science knowledge and engineering products develop as a result of the practices. Second, as instructional strategies, the practices provide a means to the learning outcomes just described and other valued outcomes such as students' understanding of the core ideas and crosscutting concepts expressed in the *Framework*. In brief, the practices represent one aspect of what students are to know, what they are able to do, and how they should be taught. Granted, this is a large order, but from the perspective of K–12, teachers will have 13 years to facilitate students' attaining the goals.

To conclude, watching the children and characters on *Sesame Street* gave me confidence that the new challenges are achievable and that K–12 science education will have a generation of boys and girls ready to engage in and learn from science and engineering practices. Preparing for the next generation of science education standards will help science teachers attain the higher aspiration of this and future generations.

Rodger W. Bybee is executive director emeritus of Biological Sciences Curriculum Study (BSCS).

References

American Association for the Advancement of Science (AAAS). 1993. *Benchmarks for Science Literacy.* Washington, DC: AAAS.

Atkin, J. M., and P. Black. 2003. *Inside science education reform: A history of curricular and policy change.* New York: Teachers College Press, Columbia University.

Black, P., and J. M. Atkin, eds. 1996. *Changing the subject: Innovations in science, mathematics and technology education.* London: Routledge.

Bybee, R., ed. 2002. *Learning science and the science of learning.* Arlington, VA: NSTA Press.

Donovan, S., and J. Bransford, eds. 2005. *How students learn: Science in the classroom.* Washington, DC: National Academies Press.

Duschl, R., H. Schweingruber, and A. Shouse, eds. 2007. *Taking science to school: Learning and teaching science in grades K–8.* Washington, DC: National Academies Press.

Engineering Concepts Curriculum Project. 1971. *The man made world.* New York: McGraw Hill.

International Technology Education Association (ITEA). 2000. *Standards for technological literacy: Content for the study of technology.* Reston, VA: Author.

Michaels, S., A. Shouse, and H. Schweingruber. 2008. *Ready, set, science!: Putting research to work in K–8 science classrooms.* Washington, DC: National Academies Press.

National Research Council (NRC). 1996. *National science education standards.* Washington, DC: National Academies Press.

National Research Council (NRC). 2000. *Inquiry and the national science education standards.* Washington, DC: National Academies Press.

National Research Council (NRC). 2011. *A framework for K–12 science education: Practices, crosscutting concepts, and core ideas.* Washington, DC: National Academies Press.

Rudolph, J. L. 2002. *Scientists in the classroom: The Cold War reconstruction of American science education.* New York: Palgrave Macmillan.

Rutherford, F. J., and A. Ahlgren. 1989. *Science for all Americans.* New York: Oxford University Press.

Core Ideas of Engineering and Technology

By Cary Sneider

Rodger Bybee's "Scientific and Engineering Practices in K–12 Classrooms" provided an overview of Chapter 3 in *A Framework for K–12 Science Education: Practices, Crosscutting Concepts, and Core Ideas* (NRC 2011). Chapter 3 describes the practices of science and engineering that students are expected to develop during 13 years of schooling and emphasizes the similarities between science and engineering.

This essay addresses Chapter 8 of the *Framework,* which presents core ideas in technology and engineering at the same level as core ideas in the traditional science fields, such as Newton's laws of motion and the theory of biological evolution. Although prior standards documents included references to engineering and technology, they tended to be separate from the "core content" of science, so they were often overlooked.

Giving equal status to engineering and technology raises a number of important issues for curriculum developers and teachers, a few of which I will discuss here:

- How does the *Framework* define *science, engineering,* and *technology?*
- What are the core ideas in Chapter 8?
- Why is there increased emphasis on engineering and technology?
- Is it redundant to have engineering practices *and* core ideas?
- Do we need to have special courses to teach these core ideas?
- Will teachers need special training?
- What will it look like in the classroom?

How does the *Framework* define *science, engineering,* and *technology?*

The meanings of these terms are summarized in the first chapter of the *Framework* as follows:

> *In the K–12 context, "science" is generally taken to mean the traditional natural sciences: physics, chemistry, biology, and (more recently) Earth, space, and environmental sciences. . . . We use the term "engineering" in a very broad sense to mean any engagement in a systematic practice of design to achieve solutions to particular human problems. Likewise, we broadly use the term "technology" to include all types of human-made systems and processes—not in the limited sense often used in schools that equates technology with modern computational and communications devices. Technologies result when engineers apply their understanding of the natural world and of human behavior to design ways to satisfy human needs and wants.* (NRC 2011, pp. 1-3, 4)

Notice that engineering is *not* defined as applied science. Although the practices of engineering have much in common with the practices of science, engineering is a distinct field and has certain core ideas that are different from those of science. Given the need to limit the number of standards so that the task for teachers and students is manageable, just two core ideas are proposed in Chapter 8. The first concerns ideas about engineering design that were not addressed in Chapter 3, and the second concerns the links among engineering, technology, science, and society.

What are the core ideas in Chapter 8?

As with core ideas in the major science disciplines, the two core ideas related to engineering and technology are first stated broadly, followed by grade band endpoints to specify what additional aspects of the core idea students are expected to learn at each succeeding level. Following are brief excerpts from the rich descriptions in the *Framework*:

Core Idea 1: Engineering Design

From a teaching and learning point of view, it is the iterative cycle of design that offers the greatest potential for applying science knowledge in the classroom and engaging in engineering practices. The components of this core idea include understanding how engineering problems are defined and delimited, how models can be used to develop and refine possible solutions to a design problem, and what methods can be employed to optimize a design. (NRC 2011, p. 8-1)

- By the end of second grade, students are expected to understand that engineering problems may have more than one solution and that some solutions are better than others.
- By the end of fifth grade, students are expected to be able to specify problems in terms of criteria for success and constraints, or limits, to understand that when solving a problem it is important to generate several different design solutions by taking relevant science knowledge into account and to improve designs through testing and modification. In some cases it is advisable to push tests to the point of failure to identify weak points.
- By the end of middle school, students should be able to recognize when it makes sense to break complex problems into manageable parts; to systematically evaluate different designs, combining the best features of each; to conduct a series of tests to refine and optimize a design solution; and to conduct simulations to test if–then scenarios.
- By the time they graduate from high school, students should be able to do all of the above and, in addition, formulate a problem with quantitative specifications; apply knowledge of both mathematics and science to develop and evaluate possible solutions; test designs using mathematical, computational, and physical models; and have opportunities to analyze the way technologies evolve through a research and development (R&D) cycle.

Core Idea 2 (Links Among Engineering, Technology, Science, and Society) has two components that are more distinct than the three components of engineering design, so they are listed separately.

Core Idea 2A: Interdependence of Science, Engineering, and Technology

The fields of science and engineering are mutually supportive. New technologies expand the reach of science, allowing the study of realms previously inaccessible to investigation; scientists depend on the work of engineers to produce the instruments and computational tools they need to conduct research. Engineers in turn depend on the work of scientists to understand how different technologies work so they can be improved; scientific discoveries are exploited to create new technologies in the first place. Scientists and engineers often work together in teams, especially in new fields, such as nanotechnology or synthetic biology that blur the lines between science and engineering. (NRC 2011, p. 8-2)

- By the end of second grade, students should know that engineers design a great many different types of tools that scientists use to make observations and measurements. Engineers also make observations and measurements to refine solutions to problems.
- By the end of fifth grade, students learn more about the role played by engineers in designing a wide variety of instruments used by scientists (e.g., balances, thermometers, graduated cylinders, telescopes, and microscopes). They also learn that scientific discoveries have led to the development of new and improved technologies.
- By the end of eighth grade, students learn that engineering advances have led to the establishment of new fields of science and entire industries. They also learn that the need to produce new and improved technologies (such as sources of energy that do not rely on fossil fuels and vaccines to prevent disease) have led to advances in science.
- By the time they graduate from high school, students should be aware of how scientists and engineers who have expertise in a number of different fields work together to solve problems to meet society's needs.

Core Idea 2B: Influence of Engineering, Technology, and Science on Society and the Natural World

The applications of science knowledge and practices to engineering, as well as to such areas as medicine and agriculture, have contributed to the technologies and the systems that support them that serve people today. . . . In turn, society influences science and engineering. Societal decisions, which may be shaped by a variety of economic, political, and cultural factors, establish goals and priorities for technologies' improvement or replacement. Such decisions also set limits—in controlling the extraction of raw materials, for example, or in setting allowable emissions of pollution from mining, farming, and industry. (NRC 2011, p. 8-1)

- By the end of second grade, students recognize that their lives depend on various technologies and that life would be very different if those technologies were to disappear. They also understand that all products are made from natural materials and that creating and using technologies have impacts on the environment.
- By the end of fifth grade, students realize that as people's needs and wants change so do their demands for new and improved technologies that drive the work of engineers. And when those new technologies are developed, they may bring about changes in the ways that people live and interact with each other.
- By the end of eighth grade, students are familiar with cases in which the development of new and improved technologies has had both positive and negative impacts on people and the environment. They understand that the development of new technologies is driven by individual and societal needs as well as by scientific discoveries and that available technologies differ from place to place and over time because of such factors as culture, climate, natural resources, and economic conditions.
- By the time they graduate from high school, students are aware of the major technological systems that support modern civilization; how engineers continually modify these systems to increase benefits while decreasing risks; and how adoption of new technologies depends on such factors as market forces, societal demands, and government support or regulation. By the end of 12th grade, students should be able to analyze costs and benefits so as to inform decisions about the development and use of new technologies.

Why is there increased emphasis on engineering and technology?

The commitment to engineering and technology in the *Framework* is extensive, as references to these terms are found throughout the document. A rationale for this increased emphasis is stated in different ways at a number of places in the *Framework*. One reason is inspirational, as described in the following paragraph:

We anticipate that the insights gained and interests provoked from studying and engaging in the practices of science and engineering during their K–12 schooling should help students see how science and engineering are instrumental in addressing major challenges that confront society today, such as generating sufficient energy, preventing and treating diseases, maintaining supplies of clean water and food, and solving the problems of global environmental change. In addition, although not all students will choose to pursue careers in science, engineering, or technology, we hope that a science education based on the Framework *will motivate and inspire a greater number of people—and a better representation of the broad diversity of the American population—to follow these paths than is the case today.* (NRC 2011, p. 1-2)

A second reason is practical. The value of developing useful knowledge and skills is summed up in the following:

> *First, the committee thinks it is important for students to explore the practical use of science, given that a singular focus on the core ideas of the disciplines would tend to shortchange the importance of applications. Second, at least at the K–8 level, these topics typically do not appear elsewhere in the curriculum and thus are neglected if not included in science instruction. Finally, engineering and technology provide a context in which students can test their own developing scientific knowledge and apply it to practical problems; doing so enhances their understanding of science—and, for many, their interest in science—as they recognize the interplay among science, engineering, and technology. We are convinced that engagement in the practices of engineering design is as much a part of learning science as engagement in the practices of science.* (NRC 2011, p. 1-4)

Is it redundant to have engineering practices *and* core ideas?

This is an excellent question, especially because there is no corresponding chapter about core ideas of scientific inquiry. However, a close reading of the *Framework* will reveal that although there is some overlap between Chapter 3 and Chapter 8, very little of the content is redundant. Chapter 3 treats engineering design as a set of practices that are similar to scientific inquiry. So students may develop these abilities in the context of asking and answering questions about the world as well as systematically solving problems. Chapter 8 expands on engineering design in ways not mentioned in Chapter 3, addressing such issues as systematically evaluating potential solutions, testing to failure, and the process of optimization.

Also, a major focus of Chapter 8 concerns the interrelationships among science, engineering, technology, society, and the environment, which are essential for all students and are not addressed anywhere else in the document. An important message of this set of core ideas is that it is important for everyone not only to know how to design technological solutions to problems, but also to think broadly about the potential impacts of new and improved technologies and to recognize the role and responsibility that all citizens have to guide the work of scientists and engineers by the decisions they make as workers, consumers, and citizens.

Do we need to have special courses to teach these core ideas?

The *Framework* provides a broad description of the content and sequence of learning expected of all students but does not provide grade-by-grade standards or specify courses at the high school level. There are many ways that these ideas can be combined and presented using a wide variety of media and learning activities. Schools are not asked to offer courses entitled "Engineering" or "Technology" any more than they are asked to offer courses with the title "Scientific Inquiry," although they may certainly do so. And although the *Next Generation Science Standards* (Achieve Inc., forthcoming) that will be based on the *Framework* will specify learning standards at a finer level of detail, it is not expected to recommend specific courses.

Will teachers need special training?

Many of the ideas about engineering and technology in the *Framework* will be familiar to today's science teachers. Many science curriculum materials include practical applications of science concepts and provide design challenges alongside science inquiry activities. Subjects such as circuit electricity and simple machines, which fall squarely in the realm of technology, have traditionally been a part of the science curriculum.

However, there will be subtle but important differences that teachers will need to become aware of. For example, design challenges are commonly presented without specific instruction in engineering design principles. Although students may have a good time and come up with creative solutions, without specific guidance they are not likely to learn about the value of defining problems in terms of criteria and constraints, how to use the problem definition to systematically evaluate alternative solutions, how to construct and test models, how to use failure analysis, or how to prioritize constraints and use trade-offs to optimize a design. Consequently, it will take some time for curriculum developers and teachers to learn about the new features of the *Framework* and incorporate these ideas into their practices. Undoubtedly the process will be greatly facilitated by inservice professional development as well as modifications of preservice preparation programs for new teachers.

What will it look like in the classroom?

There are innumerable examples in existing curricula that illustrate engineering and technology instruction at all grade levels, many in conjunction with lessons in the natural sciences. An extensive database of materials with expert teacher reviews is available via the web at the National Center for Technological Literacy (2011), hosted by the Museum of Science in Boston. The free website, called the Technology & Engineering Curriculum (TEC) Review, provides a search engine that lets teachers search by grade level, topic, or science standards to find relevant materials.

Because selecting any one of the existing materials as an example would be unfair to all the others, I've chosen to close this article with an invented example, to illustrate how the teaching of science might be enriched with an engineering activity.

Imagine a physical science class in which students are being introduced to Newton's third law, which states that every action has an equal and opposite reaction. The teacher blows up a balloon then lets it go. The balloon flies wildly around the room as air escapes out of the back end. The students are challenged to use Newton's third law to explain why the balloon flew around the room. If the students understand the basic concept, the teacher might go on to have students solve numerical problems involving Newton's third law or introduce a different topic.

Expanding on the lesson with an engineering design challenge is one way to introduce the relationship between science and engineering and to engage students in applying other concepts that they learned earlier in the year. Following the previous lesson, imagine that the teacher now asks the students to modify the balloon so that it flies more like a proper rocket—on a straight, predictable course, with as much speed and distance as possible—applying other appropriate science concepts learned previously.

Do they need to use the balloon the teacher gave them, or could they use one made from thicker rubber so they could increase the air pressure inside the balloon? Could they attach a straw and string to guide its path, or would the rocket need to fly freely? Teams would be urged to generate a number of design ideas and to evaluate them on the basis of the criteria and constraints of the problem. They would be urged to consider trade-offs as part of their planning effort; to test their designs, carefully controlling variables to determine which design works best; and to communicate the solution along with the test results that provide evidence in support of the optimal design.

Adding an engineering design challenge like the one previously described will add time to the lesson. That is not necessarily a bad thing if the science concept being applied is important to teach and challenging for students to understand without concrete examples. There are also many other approaches to introducing engineering and technology into science lessons, such as conducting research on the internet or discussing relevant current events that require less time and may focus on more important issues. And, of course, not all science ideas lend themselves easily to engineering and technology connections.

No matter how carefully new curriculum materials are designed, however, some additional time will be needed for students to apply what they are learning to the real world. Today's science curriculum is so packed that it is difficult to imagine how to add yet another set of ideas on top of what we have now. Consequently, our greatest challenge as a profession will not be whether or how to integrate engineering and technology into the curriculum, because most science educators have long considered these ideas to be an essential part of what they already do. Instead, the challenge will be how to make the difficult choices about what can safely be left out of the curriculum, so that we can do a better job of teaching core ideas and helping our students understand why they are important and how to apply them to real problems.

Cary Sneider is an associate research professor at Portland State University, Portland, Oregon. He served as the Design Team's Lead for Engineering and Technology during the development of the *Framework*.

Editor's note

The tables and page numbers referenced in this document refer to the "prepublication copy" of the *Framework* released in July 2011. A final published version will be released by the National Academies Press in late 2011 or early 2012 and will most likely have a different page-numbering system.

References

Achieve Inc. Forthcoming. *Next generation science standards*. Washington, DC: Achieve Inc.

National Center for Technological Literacy. 2011. Technology & Engineering Resources. Boston: Museum of Science. *www.mos.org/TEC.*

National Research Council (NRC). 2011. *A framework for K–12 science education: Practices, crosscutting concepts, and core ideas.* Washington, DC: National Academies Press.

The Second Dimension—Crosscutting Concepts

By Richard A. Duschl

For the last half century educators have struggled with the question, "What do we want students to know and what do they need to do to know it?" An alternative perspective for planning and framing science instruction asks "What do we want students to do and what do they need to know to do it?" The recently published National Research Council (NRC) report *A Framework for K–12 Science Education: Practices, Crosscutting Concepts, and Core Ideas* (NRC 2011) offers a thoughtful research-based agenda that helps guide us in making the shift to a doing-led agenda in K–12 science education. Grounded in the recommendations and conclusions from the NRC research synthesis report, *Taking Science to School* (NRC 2007), which I chaired, the *Framework* proposes that:

1. K–12 science education be coordinated around three intertwining dimensions: practices, crosscutting concepts, and core ideas; and
2. curricula, instruction, and assessments be aligned and then coordinated across grade band learning progressions.

In "Scientific and Engineering Practices in K–12 Classrooms," Rodger Bybee focused on scientific and engineering practices, dimension one of the *Framework*. Here the focus is on the *Framework*'s crosscutting concepts—dimension two. The *Framework* makes very clear that science learning needs to be coordinated around generative conceptual ideas and scientific practices. I begin with the seven crosscutting concepts, highlighting features within each that reveal the components of progressions. A big challenge for teachers is thinking about planning lessons and units across grade bands as student learning progresses within a grade and across grades. This will require more work, but designing lessons that move students through the crosscutting concept progression while teaching the core ideas and engaging students in the appropriate scientific practices will help ensure that students are doing science in grades K–12.

Developing an understanding of how the *Framework*'s three dimensions relate to the Four Strands of Science Proficiency in *Taking Science to School* is important. Figure 1 presents the relationships between the strands and the dimensions. The emerging evidence on science learning from *Taking Science to School*, as well as *Ready, Set, Science!* (NRC 2007, 2008) suggests the development of the science proficiencies is best supported when learning environments effectively interweave all four strands into instruction. A similar recommendation from the *Framework* is to interweave the crosscutting concepts and the scientific and engineering practices with the core ideas. What the research tells us is the primary focus for planning and instruction needs to be longer sequences of learning and teaching. The agenda is one of alignment between curriculum-instruction-assessment in classrooms where both teaching and learning is coordinated around "making thinking visible" opportunities employing talk, arguments, models, and representations. Keep this in mind as you read the overviews of the

Figure 1. Relationship of strands and dimensions (NRC 2011, p. 10-29)

Strands From Taking Science to School	Dimensions in *Framework*	How the *Framework* Is Designed to Deliver on the Commitment in the Strand
1. Knowing, using, and interpreting scientific explanations of the natural world	Disciplinary core ideas, Crosscutting concepts	Specify big ideas, not lists of facts: Core ideas in the framework are powerful explanatory ideas, not a simple list of facts, that help learners explain important aspects of the natural world. Many important ideas in science are crosscutting, and learners should recognize and use these explanatory ideas (e.g., systems) across multiple scientific contexts.
2. Generating and evaluating scientific evidence and explanations 4. Participating productively in scientific practices and discourse	Practices	Learning is defined as the combination of both knowledge and practice, not separate content and process learning goals. Core ideas in the framework are specified not as explanations to be consumed by learners. The performances combine core ideas and practices. The practices include several methods for generating and using evidence to develop, refine, and apply scientific explanations to construct accounts of scientific phenomena. Students learn and demonstrate proficiency with core ideas by engaging in these knowledge-building practices to explain and make scientifically informed decisions about the world.
3. Understanding the nature and development of scientific knowledge	Practices, Crosscutting concepts	Practices are defined as meaningful engagement with disciplinary practices, not rote procedures: Practices are defined as meaningful practices, in which learners are engaged in building, refining, and applying scientific knowledge, to understand the world, and not as rote procedures or a ritualized "scientific method." Engaging in the practices requires being guided by understandings about why scientific practices are done as they are—what counts as a good explanation, what counts as scientific evidence, how it differs from other forms of evidence, and so on. These understandings are represented in the nature of the practices and in crosscutting concepts about how scientific knowledge is developed that guide the practices.

crosscutting concepts in the next section. Ask yourself: How would I integrate the concepts into planning, teaching, and assessing science units?

The second dimension—seven crosscutting concepts

1. Patterns
2. Cause and Effect: Mechanism and Explanation
3. Scale, Proportion, and Quantity
4. Systems and System Models
5. Energy and Matter: Flows, Cycles, and Conservation
6. Structure and Function
7. Stability and Change

Look familiar? The set of crosscutting concepts in the *Framework* is similar to Unifying Concepts and Processes in the *National Science Education Standards* (NRC 1996*)*, Common Themes in *Science for All Americans* (AAAS 1989*)*, and Unifying Concepts in *Science: College Board Standards for College Success* (College Board 2009) (see Figure 2). Regardless of the labels used in these documents, each stresses, like the *Framework,* the importance that "students develop a cumulative, coherent, and usable understanding of science and engineering." (p. 4-1) The crosscutting concepts are the themes or concepts that bridge the engineering, physical, life and Earth/space sciences; in this sense they represent knowledge about science or science as a way of knowing. As such, the crosscutting concepts are very important for addressing the science literacy goals.

The first two concepts are "fundamental to the nature of science: that observed *patterns* can be explained and that science investigates *cause-and-effect* relationships by seeking the mechanisms that underlie them. The next concept—*scale, proportion, and quantity*—concerns the

Figure 2. Disciplinary bridging concepts

NSES unifying concepts	AAAS common themes	CB unifying concepts
Systems, Order, and Organization	Systems	Evolution
Evidence, Models, and Explanation	Models: Physical, Conceptual, Mathematical	Scale
Change, Constancy, and Measurement	Constancy and Change	Equilibrium
Evolution and Equilibrium	Constancy	Matter and Energy
Form and Function	Stability and Equilibrium, Conservation, Symmetry	Interaction
	Patterns of Change	Form and Function
	Trends, Cycles, Chaos	Models as Explanations, Evidence, and Representations
	Evolution	
	Possibilities, Rates, Interactions	
	Scale	

sizes of things and the mathematical relationships among disparate elements. The next four concepts—*systems and system models, energy and matter, structure and function,* and *stability and change*—are interrelated in that the first is illuminated by the other three. Each concept also stands alone as one that occurs in virtually all areas of science and is an important consideration for engineered systems as well." (NRC 2011, p. 4-2)

Progressions for teaching grades K–12

The *Framework* presents each crosscutting concept in two sections, a description followed by a synopsis statement that outlines the developmental features of increasingly sophisticated enactments by pupils. The statements below are from the crosscutting concepts chapter of the *Framework.* The grade band progression descriptions are representative and are not fixed; any one may begin sooner or later according to the development, experiences, and conceptual understandings of the students.

1. *Patterns.* **Observed patterns of forms and events guide organization and classification, and they prompt questions about relationships and the factors that influence them.**

    K–2   Pattern recognition occurs before children enter school. Develop ways to record patterns they observe. Engage pupils in describing and predicting patterns focusing on similarities and differences of characteristics and attributes.

    3–5   Classifications should become more detailed and scientific. Students should begin to analyze patterns in rates of change.

    6–8   Students begin to relate patterns to microscopic and atomic-level structures.

    9–12 Observe and recognize different patterns occurring at different scales within a system. Classifications at one scale may need revisions at other scales.

2. *Cause and effect: Mechanism and explanation.* **Events have causes, sometimes simple, sometimes multifaceted. A major activity of science is investigating and explaining causal relationships and the mechanisms by which they are mediated. Such mechanisms can then be tested across given contexts and used to predict and explain events in new contexts.**

    K–2   Children look for and analyze patterns in observations or in quantities of data. Begin to consider what may be causing the patterns.

    3–5   Students routinely ask about cause-effect relationships particularly, with unexpected results—how did that happen?

    6–8   Engage in argumentation starting from students' own cause-effect explanations and compare to scientific theories that explain causal mechanisms.

    9–12 Students argue from evidence when making a causal claim about an observed phenomenon.

3. *Scale, proportion, and quantity.* **In considering phenomena, it is critical to recognize what is relevant at different measures of size, time, and energy and to recognize how changes in scale, proportion, or quantity affect a system's structure or performance.**

K–2   Begin with objects, space, and time related to their world using explicit scale models and maps. Discuss relative scales—fastest/slowest—without reference to units of measurement. Begin to recognize proportional relationships with representations of counting, comparisons of amounts, measuring, and ordering of quantities.

3–5   Units of measurement are introduced in the context of length, building to an understanding of standard units. Extend understandings of scale and units to express quantities of weight, time, temperature, and other variables. Explore more sophisticated mathematical representations, e.g., construction and interpretation of data models and graphs.

6–8   Develop an understanding of estimation across scales and contexts. Use estimation in the examination of data. Ask if numerical results are reasonable. Develop a sense of powers of 10 scales and apply to phenomena. Apply algebraic thinking to examine scientific data and predict the effects changing one variable has on another.

9–12 Students acquire abilities to move back and forth between models at various scales and to recognize and apply more complex mathematical and statistical relationships in science.

4. *Systems and system models.* **Defining the system under study—specifying its boundaries and making explicit a model of that system—provides tools for understanding and testing ideas that are applicable throughout science and engineering.**

K–2   Express thinking using drawings and diagrams and through written and oral descriptions. Describe objects and organisms by parts; note functions and relationships of parts. Modeling supports clarifying ideas and explanations.

3–5   Create plans; draw and write instructions to build something. Models begin to reveal invisible features of a system—interactions, energy flows, matter transfers. Modeling is a tool for students to gauge their own knowledge.

6–8   Mathematical ideas—ratios, graphs—are used as tools for building models. Align grade-level mathematics to incorporate relationships among variables and some analysis of the patterns therein. Modeling reveals problems or progress in their conceptions of systems.

9–12 Identify assumptions and approximations built into models. Discuss limitations to precision and reliabilities to predictions. Modeling using mathematical relationships provides opportunities to critique models and text and to refine design ideas.

5. *Energy and matter: Flows, cycles, and conservation.* **Tracking fluxes of energy and matter into, out of, and within systems helps one understand the systems' possibilities and limitations.**

    K–2   Focus is on basic attributes of matter in examining life and Earth systems. Energy is not developed at all at this grade band.

    3–5   Macroscopic properties and states of matter, matter flows, and cycles are tracked only in terms of the weights of substances before and after a process occurs. Energy is introduced in general terms only.

    6–8   Introduce role of energy transfers with flow of matter. Mass/weight distinctions and idea of atoms and their conservation are taught. Core ideas of matter and energy inform examining systems in life science, Earth and space science, and engineering contexts.

    9–12   Fully develop energy transfers. Introduce nuclear substructure and conservation laws for nuclear processes.

6. *Structure and function.* **The way in which an object or living thing is shaped and its substructure determine many of its properties and functions.**

    K–2   Examine relationships of structure and function in accessible and visible natural and human-built systems. Progress to understandings about the relationships of structure and mechanical functions (wheels, axles, gears).

    3–5   Matter has a substructure that is related to properties of materials. Begin study of more complex systems by examining subsystems and the relationships of the parts to their functions.

    6–8   Visualize, model, and apply understandings of structure and function to more complex and less easily observable systems and processes. The concept of matter having submicroscopic structures is related to properties of matter.

    9–12   Apply the knowledge of structure and function when investigating unfamiliar phenomena; when building something or deciphering how a system works, begin with examining what it is made of and what shapes its parts take.

7. *Stability and change.* **For natural and built systems alike, conditions of stability and determinants of rates of change or evolution of the system are critical elements of study.**

    K–2   Children arrive to school having explored stability and change. Develop language for these concepts and apply across multiple examples. Help foster asking questions about why change both does and does not happen.

    3–5   Explore explanations for regularities of a pattern over time or its variability. A good model for a system should demonstrate how stability and change are related and offer an explanation for both.

    6–8   As understanding of matter progresses to the atomic scale, so too should models and explanations of stability and change. Begin to engage in more subtle or conditional situations and the need for feedback to maintain a system.

9–12   Students can model even more complex systems and attend to more subtle issues of stability and change. Examine the construction of historical explanations that account for the way things are today by modeling rates of change and conditions when systems are stable or change gradually, accounting for sudden changes, too.

The message from the *Framework* is that there are important interconnections between crosscutting concepts and disciplinary core ideas. "Students' understandings of these crosscutting concepts should be reinforced by repeated use in the context of instruction in the disciplinary core ideas... the crosscutting concepts can provide a connective structure that supports students' understanding of sciences as disciplines and that facilitates their comprehension of the systems under study in particular disciplines" (p. 4-13). What this says is that the crosscutting concepts are to be embedded within and conjoined across coherent sequences of science instruction. The *Framework's* three dimensions—science practices, crosscutting concepts, core ideas—send a clear message that science learning and instruction must not separate the knowing (concepts, ideas) from the doing (practices). Thus, the assessment strategies teachers adopt for pupils' understandings of and enactments with the seven crosscutting concepts must also conjoin the knowing and doing.

Assessing crosscutting concept learning with learning performances

The *Framework's* three dimensions represent a more integrated view of science learning that should reflect and encourage science activity that approximates the practices of scientists. What that means for the crosscutting concepts is that assessment tasks should be cumulative across a grade band and contain many of the social and conceptual characteristics of what it means to "do" science; e.g., talk and arguments, modeling and representations. The assessments of crosscutting concepts would be less frequent; each term or annually there would be a performance assessment task that would reveal how students are enacting and using the three dimensions. The majority of assessment tasks for crosscutting concepts will be constructed-response and performance assessments. If the goal is to gauge students' enactments of crosscutting concepts when asked to ascertain patterns, generate mechanisms and explanations, distinguish between stability and change, provide scale representations, model data, and otherwise engage in various aspects of science practices, then the students must show evidence of "doing" science and of critiquing and communicating what was done.

The *Framework* provides teachers with an agreed upon set of curricular goals. The *Next Generation Science Standards* (*NGSS*) assessments will be in a "learning performances" format. For example, consider a task to explain how a smell travels through a room. It could be assessed using the grade band information described in section 5, Energy and Matter: Flow, Cycles, and Conservation. The expectation is for students to use some conceptual knowledge (e.g., states of matter) with a practice (e.g., modeling) to develop a mechanism (gas/particle diffusion) that explains the odor's movement. What a teacher is seeking is evidence that students are developing a model of matter made of particles. Related tasks could be mechanisms for the diffusion of a colored dye in water, the separation of sediments in water, or the role of limiting factors in an ecosystem or chemical reaction. The tasks can be gathered over the grade band to develop a portfolio of evidence about students' understandings and enactments of crosscutting concepts.

Summary

The inclusion of crosscutting concepts in the *Framework* continues a 50-year history in U.S. science education that both scientific knowledge and knowledge about science are important K–12 science education goals. It's the dual agenda for science. The crosscutting concepts are best thought of as the learning goals for science literacy. But success hinges on doing the science. The coordination of the three dimensions reinforces the importance of not separating the doing from the knowing. The alignment of curriculum-instruction-assessment models coordinated around learning progression ideas and research has great potential to organize classrooms and other learning environments around adaptive instruction (targeted feedback to students) and instructed-assisted development. In science over the last century, we have learned how to learn about nature. In education over the last century, we have learned how to learn about learning. As we proceed deeper into the 21st century, let us learn how to meld together these two endeavors. The *Framework* and the forthcoming *NGSS* are a great beginning, but successful implementation will only come about through the participation and commitment of teachers.

The shift to a "doing" science curriculum focus enacted through the seven crosscutting concepts and the eight scientific and engineering practices will provide students with experiences over weeks, months, and years that will shape their images about the crosscutting concepts, the practices, and, thus, the nature of science. The teacher is the key that will help us unlock how to fully understand the best coherent sequences for learning and teaching.

Richard A. Duschl is the Waterbury Chair of Secondary Education at The Pennsylvania State University, and co-chair of the Earth/Space Science writing team for the *Next Generation Science Standards*.

References

American Association for the Advancement of Science (AAAS). 1989. *Science for all Americans.* New York: Oxford University Press.

College Board. 2009. *Science: College Board standards for college success. http://professionals.collegeboard. com/profdownload/cbscs-science-standards-2009.pdf*

National Research Council (NRC). 2007. *Taking science to school: Learning and teaching science in grades K–8.* Washington, DC: National Academies Press.

National Research Council (NRC). 2008. *Ready, set, science! Putting research to work in K–8 science classrooms.* Washington, DC: National Academies Press.

National Research Council (NRC). 2011. *A framework for K–12 science education: Practices, crosscutting concepts, and core ideas.* Washington, DC: National Academies Press.

Engaging Students in Scientific Practices: What Does Constructing and Revising Models Look Like in the Science Classroom?

By Joseph Krajcik and Joi Merritt

The *Next Generation Science Standards (NGSS)*—now in development—will be based on *A Framework for K–12 Science Education* released by the National Research Council last summer. The *NGSS* will use four key ideas from the *Framework*: (1) a limited number of core ideas of science, (2) the integration or coupling of core ideas and scientific and engineering practices, (3) crosscutting concepts, and (4) the development of the core ideas, scientific practices, and crosscutting concepts over time.

In "Scientific and Engineering Practices in K–12 Classrooms," Rodger Bybee provided an overview of the scientific and engineering practices and showed how they are a refinement and further articulation of what it means to do scientific inquiry in the science classroom (2011).

The *Framework* identifies seven scientific and engineering practices that should be used in science classrooms. These practices reflect the multiple ways in which scientists explore and understand the world and the multiple ways in which engineers solve problems. These practices include:

- Asking questions (for science) and defining problems (for engineering)
- Developing and using models
- Planning and carrying out investigations
- Analyzing and interpreting data
- Using mathematics, information and computer technology, and computational thinking
- Constructing explanations (for science) and designing solutions (for engineering)
- Engaging in argument from evidence
- Obtaining, evaluating, and communicating information

Here, we look in-depth at scientific practice #2—developing, evaluating, and revising scientific models to explain and predict phenomena—and what it means for classroom teaching. Models provide scientists and engineers with tools for thinking, to visualize and make sense of phenomena and experience, or to develop possible solutions to design problems (NRC 2011). Models are external representations of mental concepts. Models can include diagrams, three-dimensional physical structures, computer simulations, mathematical formulations, and analogies. It is challenging for learners to understand that all models only approximate and simplify how the entities they represent work, yet models provide a powerful tool of explaining phenomena. It's critical that a model be consistent with the evidence that exists, and that different models are appropriate in different situations depending on what is being explained.

If the model cannot account for the evidence, then the model should be abandoned (Schwarz et al. 2009).

A Framework for K–12 Science Education states that by the end of the 12th grade students should be able to:

- Construct drawings or diagrams as representations of events or systems.
- Represent and explain phenomena with multiple types of models and move flexibly between model types when different ones are most useful for different purposes.
- Discuss the limitations and precision of a model as the representation of a system, process, or design and suggest ways in which the model might be improved to better fit available evidence or better reflect a design's specifications. Refine a model in light of empirical evidence or criticism to improve its quality and explanatory power.
- Use (provided) computer simulations or simulations developed with simple simulation tools as a tool for understanding and investigating aspects of a system, particularly those not readily visible to the naked eye.
- Make and use a model to test a design, or aspects of a design, and to compare the effectiveness of different design solutions. (NRC 2011, p. 3-20).

What does this practice mean for classroom instruction? What does it mean that the practices of modeling will be blended with core ideas? Perhaps the biggest change the modeling practice brings to classroom teaching is the expectation for students to construct and revise models based on new evidence to predict and explain phenomena and to test solutions to various design problems in the context of learning and using core ideas. Students will be engaged in what it means to do science because this is one major activity that drives scientific work and thinking.

Often in science class, students are given the final, canonical scientific model that scientists have developed over numerous years, and little time is spent showing them the evidence for the model or allowing them to construct models that will explain phenomena. As a result, often learners do not see a difference between the scientific model and the phenomena the model is predicting and explaining, or the value of the model for explaining and finding solutions. The *Framework* emphasizes that multiple models might explain a phenomena and that students should improve models to fit new evidence. It is important that science teachers engage students in the modeling process. What do modeling practices look like in the classroom? What are teachers expected to do in their teaching?

It is important for students to construct models that explain phenomena, show how their models are consistent with their evidence, and explain the limitations of those models. Following is one example of what this might look like in a middle school classroom. Imagine a sixth-grade class engaged in exploring core ideas from the *Framework*'s PS1.A: "Gases and liquids are made of molecules or inert atoms that are moving about relative to each other. In a liquid, the molecules are constantly in contact with others; in a gas, they are widely spaced except when they happen to collide." (NRC 2011, p. 5-4). Blending this core idea with the practice of constructing and revising models, students could be asked to draw a model of how the odor gets from the source to your nose (Merritt and Krajcik 2012; Merritt 2010). Students are asked to complete the task described in Figure 1.

Students are asked to make this model three times during an eight-week unit that focuses on Core Idea PS1.A. In each case, students need to include a key, the drawing, and an explanation of the drawing. Students construct their first model on the first day of the unit. Students walk into class, and the teacher opens a container that contains a strong odor (typically menthol) and asks the students to make a drawing (a representation) of how the odor gets from the container to their noses. The students have had no formal instruction on the particle nature of matter. All they are expected to do is draw a feasible model consistent with the evidence they might see if they had a very powerful instrument that would allow them to "see" the odor.

Typically at this initial stage, students' models do not match the scientific model. This is perfectly okay as long as the student model is reasonable and feasible. As previously reported (Novick and Nussbaum 1978), students initially draw a continuous or cloud model to represent the air and the odor. Figure 2 shows an example of what students typically draw.

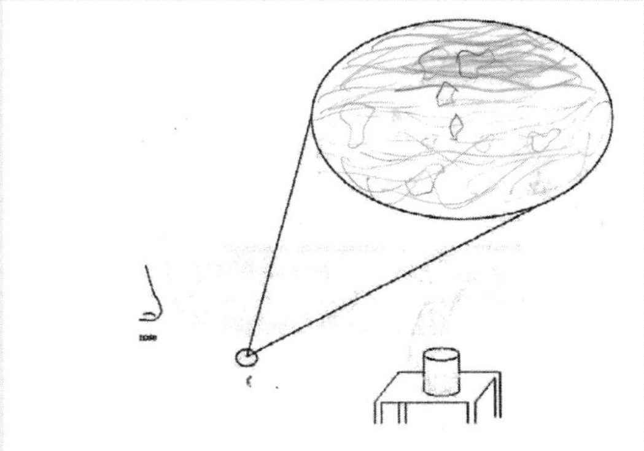

Next, students complete a series of investigations in which they explore properties of gases. For instance, they use syringes to experience that gases are compressible and expandable: You can add gas to or remove it from a container with a fixed volume without changing the shape of the container. Using these and related experiences, students are again challenged to create a new model of matter to explain how an odor can get from a source to their noses and what they would see if they had a special

Figure 1. Drawing a model of an odor.

Imagine that you have a special instrument that allows you to see what makes up odor. The large circle in the drawing below represents a spot that is magnified many times, so you can see it up close. Create a model of what you would see if you could focus on one tiny spot in the area between the jar and your nose.

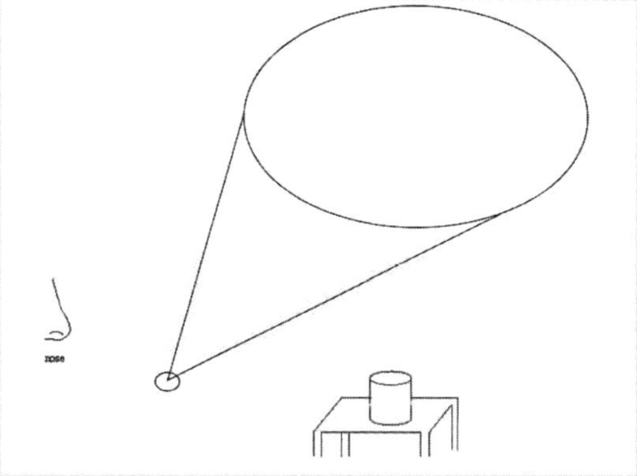

Label the parts of your model, so someone who looks at it will know what the parts represent.

Figure 2. A student model at the initial stage.

4. Label what the parts in your drawing represent.

instrument that "sees" odor. Now, however, their models must be consistent with the evidence they have regarding the properties of gases (i.e., gases can be expanded and compressed and can be added to or taken away from a container with a fixed volume). As Figure 3 shows, students now draw models that are more particulate in nature.

Figure 3. A student's second attempt at drawing a model of air and odor.

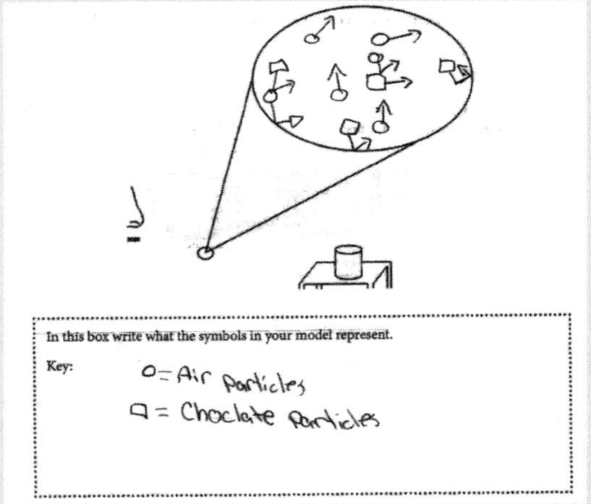

In this box write what the symbols in your model represent.

Key:
O = Air particles
◻ = Choclate Particles

Figure 4. A student's model at the end of the unit.

2. Label the parts in your drawing.

KEY:
△ = Air Particles
◻ = odor
→ = Path
◻ = nothing

White Space

Although this model is still not consistent with the full scientific model, it has features consistent with scientific models. The student now visualizes air and odor to consist of tiny particles too small to see; the particles have space between them and travel in straight lines until they collide with other particles. There are some concerns with the model. For instance, the model shows particles that collide with the imaginary side of the magnified section. The model, however, is consistent with the evidence the student has collected: that a gas can be compressed, expanded, and added to or taken away from a container with a fixed volume.

Throughout the unit, students continue to collect additional evidence about the properties of gases. For instance, students explore the effect of temperature on how fast a gas travels by investigating the time it takes ammonia vapor to change indicator paper blue when a test tube containing drops of ammonia is in a warm versus cool water bath. Once students have developed their own models, through careful scaffolding by the teacher, they also develop a class consensus model and explore computer simulations to develop a rich and integrated model of the structure of gases, liquids, and solids as being particulate in nature.

As Figure 4 indicates, at the end of the unit most students have developed models more consistent with the scientific model. The model in Figure 4 shows that gases (air and odor) are made up of tiny particles too small to see, have space between them, move and collide into each other, and change direction as a result of these collisions. There is no indication of the particles colliding with the imaginary walls of the magnified section. Moreover, the student clearly points out there is nothing between the particles. These understandings form a foundation that can be used to build more sophisticated models of the structure of matter. What is important to realize in these examples is that these student models account for all the evidence they have regarding the properties of gases. The student was not told the features of the particle model but rather developed the particle model through carefully supported modeling activities in which students built models based upon evidence. This is the major feature of the modeling practice: developing and revising models.

Concluding comment

Because *A Framework for K–12 Science Education* emphasizes fewer ideas developed across K–12 science curriculum and blended with the use of scientific practices and crosscutting elements, *Next Generation Science Standards* will present a more coherent view of science education that will engage students in the process of doing science.

The U.S. science curriculum has long suffered from being disconnected and presenting too many ideas too superficially, often leaving students with disconnected ideas that cannot be used to solve problems and explain phenomena they encounter in their everyday world. John Dewey expressed this concern in 1910, and we continue to strive so that students learn science in a more coherent manner.

> *Science teaching has suffered because science has been so frequently presented just as so much ready-made knowledge, so much subject-matter of fact and law, rather than as the effective method of inquiry into any subject-matter.* (Dewey 1910)

By focusing on big ideas blended with practices and crosscutting elements over time, the *Framework* and *Next Generation Science Standards* strive to avoid shallow coverage of a large number of topics and allow more time for students to explore and examine ideas in greater depth and use those ideas to understand phenomena they encounter in their lives, while engaging in an "effective method of inquiry." The modeling practices and the example described in this article demonstrate science teaching as "effective method of inquiry into any subject-matter." This focus on fewer ideas blended with scientific and engineering practices will allow teachers and students time to do science by engaging in a range of scientific practices, including creating and revising models that can explain phenomena and that change as more evidence is collected. Imagine the type of student who emerges from 12th-grade science education after repeatedly experiencing instruction since elementary school that supported them in constructing and revising models to explain phenomena! These students will form a different breed of high school graduates who view science as an "effective method of inquiry" and who will serve as productive 21st-century citizens to create a sustainable planet.

Joseph Krajcik is a professor of science education, and *Joi Merritt* is a postdoctoral researcher focusing on science education, both at Michigan State University. Krajcik served as Design Team Lead for the *Framework* and currently serves as Design Team Lead for the Next Generation Science Standards.

References

Bybee, R. 2011. Scientific and engineering practices in K–12 classrooms: Understanding *A Framework for K–12 Science Education*. *Science and Children* 49 (4): 10–15.

Dewey, J. 1910. Science as subject matter and method. *Science* 31 (787): 121–127.

Merritt, J. 2010. Tracking students' understanding of the particle nature of matter. Doctoral dissertation. University of Michigan, Ann Arbor, MI.

Merritt, J., and J.S. Krajcik. 2012. Supporting students in building a particle model of matter. In *Structural Concepts of Matter in Science Education* (forthcoming), eds. G. Tsaparlis and H. Sevian. Dordrecht, Netherlands: Springer.

National Research Council (NRC). 2011. *A framework for K–12 science education: Practices, crosscutting concepts, and core ideas*. Washington, DC: National Academies Press.

Novick, S., and J. Nussbaum. 1978. Junior high school pupils' understanding of the particulate nature of matter: An interview study. *Science Education* 62 (3): 273–281.

Schwarz, C., B. Reiser, E. Davis, L. Kenyon, A. Acher, D. Fortus, Y. Shwartz, B. Hug, and J.S. Krajcik. 2009. Developing a learning progression for scientific modeling: Making scientific modeling accessible and meaningful for learners. *Journal of Research in Science Teaching* 46 (1): 232–254.

NSTA believes the *Framework* provides valuable guidance and recommendations to encourage the development of standards that allow for the teaching of science in greater depth. We are a committed partner in the process of developing new standards and will stay involved to ensure that the voices of science educators are heard and that the *NGSS* are the best they can be.

NSTA is developing extensive resources to help science educators and other stakeholders address the changes that the *Framework* and the upcoming *Next Generation Science Standards* will bring. All resources will be available online at *www.nsta.org/ngss*. Also look for updates in NSTA's four member journals as well as in *NSTA Express* and *NSTA Reports*.

Index

D